Best Practices for Farmers and Gardeners

The NOFA handbook series is designed to give a comprehensive view of key farming practices from the organic perspective. The content is geared to serious farmers, gardeners and homesteaders and those looking to make the organic transition.

Many of these folks have arrived at their own best methods to suit their situations of place and pocketbook. These handbooks may help practitioners review and reconsider their concepts and practices in light of holistic biological realities, classic works and recent research.

Organic agriculture has deep roots and a complex paradigm that stands in bold contrast to the industrialized conventional agriculture dominating today. It's critical that organic farming get a fair hearing in the public arena—and that farmers have access not only to the real dirt of organic methods and practices but also to the concepts behind them.

Where This Series Comes From

The Northeast Organic Farming Association (NOFA) is one of the oldest organic agriculture organizations in the country, dedicated to organic food production and a safer, healthier environment.

NOFA has independent chapters in Connecticut, Massachusetts, New Hampshire, New Jersey, New York, Rhode Island, and Vermont.

This handbook series began with a gift to NOFA/Mass and continues under the NOFA Interstate Council with support from NOFA/Mass and a generous grant from Sustainable Agriculture Research and Education (SARE). The project, which currently stands at ten titles, has utilized the expertise of NOFA members and other organic farmers and educators in the Northeast as writers and editors. Help also came from the Pennsylvania Association for Sustainable Agriculture and from the Maine Organic Farmers and Gardeners Association.

Jocelyn Langer illustrated the series and Jonathan von Ranson edited it and coordinated the project. The Manuals Project Committee included Bill Duesing, Steve Gilman, Elizabeth Henderson, Julie Rawson and Jonathan von Ranson. The Committee thanks SARE and the wonderful farmers and educators whose willing commitment it represents.

Contents

Author Rebecca Bosch is an entrepreneur, writer and nutrition activist. "Good Stuff by Mom & Me," the business that she began with—you guessed it—mom, produces low processed organic, raw, gluten-free foods and offers periodic classes in diet and lifestyle change. To reach her, e-mail foodalive@yahoo.com or call 888 797-6865. Rebecca makes her home in Ithaca, N.Y.

Illustrator Jocelyn Langer is an artist, music teacher and organic gardener, and the illustrator of the nine other NOFA organic farming handbooks in this series. She illustrates and does graphic design work for alternative media and political events as well as organic farming-related publications. Jocelyn lives in central Mass.

Special farmer-reviewer **George DeVault**
Scientific reviewer **John W. Berry**

Foreword

My dad grew up in a town that had the same name as the town where I was raised, but his town was different than mine. In his town every other homestead was a small farm. His mom got her eggs at the house down the road; she dipped her milk out of a bulk tank around the corner; my dad made pocket money picking potatoes a few doors away after school.

In my town, it was difficult to find a teenager who worked outside, or a family that did not purchase everything from the local grocery and convenience chains. In my town, few working farms remained.

My dad's town brings him memories rich with people, shared resources and seasonality. Mine seemed more anonymous: McDonalds and Pizza Hut, farms too mechanized for kids, busy suburban roads encouraging us off our feet and into cars. Strawberries on demand.

I grew up on one of the few small farms remaining in the area. The kids whose parents commuted the two-hour round trip to Buffalo examined me with a mix of awe and alarm when they learned that I did chores before school. Milking goats and working in the garden were exotic to many of them. Our new neighbors—attracted by dreams of country living—were buying up productive farmland as Buffalo's sprawl lapped the shores of Wyoming County's dairy farms somewhere around our doorstep. Farmers unwilling to mortgage and expand were forced to join the morning commute.

My town is an echo of my dad's. The tatters of a local farm economy play on the wind of growth and change. Today the local Agway is split down the middle, offering high-brow wine dinners on one side and latte frappuccinos on the other.

One of the most hopeful elements in the picture is the effort that's arising—organically—to reclaim local relevance, scale and spirit. On Wednesdays and Saturdays, the farmers' market teems with activity; Tuesdays and Thursdays are pick-up days for two local community supported farms, and every day offers farm stands and you-pick opportunities from first to final harvest. A new co-op is being built to provide the community with local, low processed foods.

My town is feeling the excitement of change, rediscovering the richness of community in conversations across the farm stand, in the CSA parking lot and over dinner. I can't wait to see what we make of it.

Chapter 1
Introduction

The last century is an astonishing tale of acceleration. In one human lifespan we have absorbed cars, radio, television, refrigeration, flight, microwaves, computers and other technologies so completely that kids today cannot imagine living without them. These innovations have revolutionized our lives, but their impacts on human health and nature as a whole raise questions about their ultimate value. Eighty per cent of our diseases, medical experts say, are directly linked to frantic living. Little surprise; how could any living thing not reflect the stress of such a swift and sweeping transformation?

There are other tangible concerns. In 2002 the *New York Times* reported that land degradation from deforestation, waste disposal and overuse of fertilizers has rendered a third of the earth's soil unfit for growing food. Over a third of U.S. rivers, lakes and estuaries are unsafe for swimming and fishing and unable to provide a healthy habitat for fish and other water-dependent wildlife (U.S.Public Interest Research Group). Voices worldwide warn of an impending global freshwater crisis as glaciers melt and groundwater is poisoned by pesticides, fertilizers, industrial chemicals and septic systems. The global warming effect we're experiencing traces back to the power plants, automobiles and industry that have become the hallmarks of our "advancement."

Ordinary human beings have depreciated in value before this system, pushed aside along with our traditional cottage industries and small farms. As demand is manipulated from afar and production is geared to export, the former rhythm and interplay of rural life are becoming a scrambling balance between poverty, survival and fickle market forces. The suffering is international as the demand for open markets and cheap products break traditional ties to earth-based livelihoods. In India, more than 25,000 debt-ridden peasant farmers have taken their own lives since 1997, demoralized by the loss of control of their seed sources (to multinational corporations), commodity prices (to the influence of the World Trade Organization) and crop failures (to violent weather and drought). They are not alone.

Yes, but...you may well be wondering...where does marketing fit in? Marketing—fundamentally the art of developing a product or service (be it haircuts, cheese or snake oil) and convincing people to buy it—has evolved a technology of created demand that has become a most powerful social stimulant. It is now ubiquitous, a mechanism shaping our local and global structures, economic and otherwise.

As we begin to understand the global price we're paying, exploitive marketing and unchecked consumption are being recognized as ever-greater threats to planetary citizenship. In marketing, many of us now see the peddler of dissatisfaction and desire: contriving, encouraging, enticing, enthralling, enlisting and alluring individuals to buy something—anything. To buy it now (if you want to be considered fully human!) and buy it often, never mind if you're doing yourself in!

This kind of head-down marketing is largely responsible for my town's experience as described in the Foreword. It will play a pivitol role in what my town—every town—will be tomorrow. But in certain quarters marketing has been getting a makeover. A forward-thinking approach supports a marketing strategy for making a living without subverting our shared future. That goal is what this handbook is all about.

Changing the business of business

> Arise, come, hasten, let us abandon the city to merchants, attorneys, brokers, usurers, tax-gatherers, scriveners, doctors, perfumers, butchers, cooks, bakers and tailors, alchemists, painters, mimes, dancers, lute-players, quacks, panderers, thieves, criminals, adulterers, parasites, foreigners, swindlers and jesters, gluttons who with scent alert catch the odor of the market place, for whom that is the only bliss, whose mouths are agape for that alone.

> —Francesco Petrarch, *De Vita Solitaria,* 1356

This manual focuses on the nuts of bolts of marketing in a new context: one that recognizes the crucial role we as businesspeople play in social evolution and the demand now awakening for responsible commercial behavior. There is a healing approach to commerce that works. In a sense, it involves reacquainting our various compartmentalized selves with each other—my inner entrepreneur, for example, with the community member that's inside me too; my competitive spirit with the nurturer in there, the one who would go hungry to feed a child. Giving a damn about real-world conditions is the motivation for this inner block party. Businesspeople who manifest this kind of healthy pragmatism and caring are already inventing a more balanced approach to marketing.

Basically it's easy to get too single-minded about business. Let's take a good look at why that tendency might not serve you, even as an entrepreneur.

As a nation, we are still experimenting with a relatively pure form of capitalism, defined by the American Heritage Dictionary as:

> *An economic system characterized by freedom of the market with increasing concentration of private and corporate ownership of production and distribution means, proportionate to increasing accumulation and reinvestment of profits.*

Incredibly successful by capitalist measures, we operated for decades by the idea that every generation would achieve greater material wealth than its predecessor. This linear imperative, called growth, broke ancient cultural constraints and fueled a comprehensive national shift in the last half of the 20th century from production to consumption, rural to suburban living and local to global markets.

Capitalist theory says excesses of commercial interests are mitigated through the strength of the consumer dollar. But what if those dollars get sparse for most—concentrated, as predicted in the definition above, into a few hands? What happens to the have-nots: their perspective, their "vote"? And how effective has the oversight supposedly offered by supply and demand been?

Robert McChesney (*The Problem of the Media*) contends that products and services available on the market do not represent true public value and concern. His view is that the market provides what the public wants within the limited range of what has market value—in dollars—right now. Though each product has a cost in social, environmental and energy-use values, these costs are unspecified, hard to measure and individually easy to dismiss. Thus, industry offers products based on their profit potential, valuing low overhead and cheap labor over concerns that resist monetary evaluation such as longevity, stability, environmental and social quality of life and diversity.

There are other challenges to the free market ideal, like misleading marketing practices. Others are government-sponsored subsidies, tax breaks and trade regulations that favor corporate and industry interests.

Great, holistic values haven't shown up in the marketplace model—the system as practiced has been antithetical to them. Imagine going out and purchasing a vibrant community, functioning ecologically within a bioregion, as you can an automobile—with or without a warranty!? "Sorry, ma'am, we're out of those right now…"

At its best, capitalism is a celebration of human capability. By taking the next step, by folding the unmarketable gifts of life into their practice, businesspeople have an opportunity to qualitatively improve their own lives and resurrect our collective future.

It is high time for critical self-evaluation. Tradition does not excuse lies—of omission or commission—to ourselves and to our customers. Only sober, accurately informed participants can create a free market system that offers a viable future, in which societal interest takes its proper place above the narrow desires of persons or corporations.

Re-elevating The Nurturer

Wendell Berry distinguishes upside-down economic motives from life-sustaining ones in his reflection, *A Continuous Harmony*:

> *The standard of the exploiter is efficiency; the standard of the nurturer is care. The exploiter's goal is money, profit; the nurturer's goal is health—his land's health, his own, his family's, his community's, his country's... The exploiter wishes to earn as much as possible by as little work as possible; the nurturer expects, certainly, to have a decent living from his work, but his characteristic wish is to work as well as possible. The competence of the exploiter is in organization; that of the nurturer is in order... The exploiter typically serves an institution or organization; the nurturer serves land, household, community, place. The exploiter thinks in terms of numbers, quantities, "hard facts"; the nurturer in terms of character, condition, quality, kind... The exploitive always involves the abuse or the perversion of nurture.*

The exploiter has dominated, but today voices of nurturance penetrate the din of commerce. One of them, activist Kevin Danaher—the cofounder of Global Exchange—spearheads the Fair Trade™ campaign to provide an equitable distribution of profit to producers worldwide. Developed to curb the exploitation of third world farmers by global markets, this initiative is instructive to U.S. farmers, who receive no more than nine cents of the average consumer food dollar, down from the 35 cents they received just three decades ago (Salatin, 1998). Intermediaries are getting the difference. They deserve fair compensation for work too, but Global Exchange and others argue that the clamor for low retail prices creates an elastic global commodity market that undermines land-based economies, exacerbates instability and concentrates profits out of the hands of producers and into large-scale corporate bank accounts.

Fair Trade-certified coffee, chocolate, bananas and a number of other products are now available in a growing number of retail outlets throughout the country. Fair Trade is an example of novel market thinking: the incorporation of a nurturing impulse—basic fairness—to bring about revolutionary change in the marketplace.

Marketing and common responsibility

The global nature of our activities has expanded what writer Garret Harden named "the commons"—the free, natural goodness (e.g., clean rivers, the living planet). In *The Tragedy of the Commons* he describes how they fall victim to the individual greed permitted in our economic system. It has become clear that unbounded desires are not alone in fouling common resources: population growth is a factor, as is the displacement from the land of a newly dependent urban, consumer population. It's important to realize the Earth doesn't just sit and watch this happen. There are natural laws always working to limit the concentration of individual control and reestablish common balance. Their enforcement is gradual but relentless, and we have a poor record for anticipating the long-term effects of our actions. Organic marketers know not to fight these natural commandments, they make friends with them, tie their practices to them. The spirit of the laws permeates the marketer's encompassing motives.

Successful fair trade initiatives are showing us that capitalism can respond to endangerment of our common resources when patrons become convinced of the value of protecting them and are given the opportunity to do so. The movement (it can now be called one) is showing that informed buyers cast their votes in the marketplace not only in exchange for goods and services, but also for fairness and integrity. Marketing itself has improved awareness of certain great concerns, encouraged responsible choices and provided them. This is the power of personal accountability that Gandhi evoked when he called on us to "be the change you wish to see in the world." To address the great problems as we shape our marketing approach is, for us in organic food production, to vote with our day-to-day efforts.

Assumptions of conventional marketing

These are some of the assumptions of the dominant commercial system today:

Human Entitlement. We humans misjudge our place in nature, seeing it as a mechanical system put there for us to tinker with when it might be better described as a living web of which we're a few short strands. Even small influences can balloon to large consequences, and our big initiatives to control nature and our place in it have spelled disequilibrium, broken strands. Industry has been implicated in species extinction; erratic weather patterns; global climate change; the expanding hole in the ozone layer; and degenerative disease.

Scientific Authority as Reliable Guide. Our ability to understand and manage our lives is bound to an inescapable truth—our scale as a species. We're of medium size flanked by indeterminate macro- and microcosms. Training our telescopes above and our microscopes below, we periodically revamp scientific understandings…at the same time we deal with the oops! factor of earlier scientific "truths" expressed in our technologies and public policies. All the while we face the press of accelerating economic exchange, new societal demands and environmental distresses. *Modern* may sound reassuring, but the science we honor by this year's technology is still selective, our means are still experimental and catch-up and the industrial approach—behind the Wizard-of-Oz curtain—remains terribly imperfect and often downright harmful.

Independence. We have been weaned on the mythology of the self-made millionaire, but *inter*dependence is us. Not only do we rely on one another, but we also rely on the natural world for all the resources we require for our survival. Reflecting that 44 million American adults are obese and an additional 6 million are super-obese (weighing over 100 pounds more than they should) Eric Schlosser reports that "No other nation in history has gotten so fat so fast." (Eric Schlosser, Fast Food Nation). Fueled by incentives to buy and consume MORE, the essence of our national philosophy shows up even in the average American physique. How can we doubt that everything is connected?

Time Is Money. Ready for a shock? Time is not money. Time is free… Binding it to money makes everything else expensive. Money-time measures out fellowship and relationships in dollar bills. Imagine if time was matched with a different partner: time is love, time is family, time is communal life. What different worlds would be created by these subtle changes in our habit of thought! Asian Theologian Kosuke Koyama describes the effects of this market concept on quality of life:

> *Time in Asia was traditionally experienced as being as unlimited as a loving mother's milk is unlimited to her baby. Time was generously given. It was not sold as pork chops are sold…Time was cyclical, that is to say, calm and level-headed…it was communal.*
>
> *Now, this has been changed without any consultation with us!… Time is now located in the export-import companies, motorcycle manufacturers, stores and shops… It is now private business property. Once it was shared, now it is monopolized. Time does not heal us now. Time wounds us.*

Assumptions of sustainable marketing

These are some of the assumptions underlying a commercial exchange system that's sustainable (I'll sometimes refer to it as organic, fitting with the natural laws):

Quality. The focus on quality is key. It necessitates a total rehab of the assumptions and methods that underly your business: a commitment to practices that serve your own true quality of life and your circle of influence, ones that consider your needs—current and future location-based concerns. The premise is that profit is, at most, a small part of life's quality.

Natural Limits. An illustration of natural laws and their immutability comes from Steven Covey's *Seven Habits of Highly Effective People*:

> *A gunboat—the Missouri—is surprised to find itself on a collision course with another ship one night at sea. The two ships angrily refuse to change course to make way for each other, until collision is imminent. Enraged, the Captain demands that the other commander break course to starboard, to make way for "the mighty Missouri." "Starboard, yourself," replied the other, "This is the lighthouse."*

Natural laws are life's basic principles that apply to all situations. They are like the lighthouse; we cannot break them, though—in fooling ourselves—we can break ourselves upon them. The sustainable course in marketing begins with a humble openness to how the world itself operates, on principles like those that we see in the wild such as:

- **self-renewal through completed cycles and no waste**
- **a balance of cooperation and competition: taking, giving, leaving alone...**

It is fundamental to know that our businesses function in a thin envelope where natural resources are limited and waste is a foreign concept before offering products, services, packaging or promotion. The fact that people will spend money for it does not mean it is a responsible offering: is it needed, or does it deplete resources beyond its real value?

You have your own natural limits: your level of experience, the capabilities of your body and your conscience all have their own parameters. Carefully observed, these are palpable realities by which to guide your enterprise. Another limit is the pace at which your business can reasonably grow. Farming itself is a testament to nature's pace, one that reproaches pressure—such as the use of hormones and chemical fertilizers—with harvests of physical and nutritive impoverishment. Attention to natural limits involves balance, a sense of consequence and judgment. The nature of your own unique situation is the foundation for your business.

Enough. Setting one's financial "enough" is expressing one's truthful interaction with the world. The farming enterprise has been weighted by convention toward the idea of selling more to profit more. Yet there have always been at least two ways to increase our riches: to acquire great wealth or to acquire few needs. Thoreau challenges us to "learn what are the necessaries, [as] most of the luxuries and many of the so-called comforts are not only dispensable but positive hindrances." This is not to relegate yourself to a life of abject poverty, but to adjust the scale of your efforts to a conscious determination of your "necessaries." To accumulate affluence draws upon the common resource base as well as your time, energy and concern. By settling the issue of your life essentials, you can determine the level of profit required as well as the production capacity and market considerations necessary to achieve it.

Enough provides you with the expectation of completion: freedom from fiscal compulsion—a relief denied to people in growth-based enterprises.

Responsibility. When making marketing decisions, we businessfolk are more susceptible to the siren call of profit than at any other time in our ventures. One can make a great deal of profit at the expense of others, but no spin of marketing ethics can fudge the imperative of every person's responsibility for their own actions. In organic marketing, our business stands as a recognizable presence that does not hide behind corporate anonymity, defile our common resources, or trample others in pursuit of profit or capital.

Interconnection. Sustainable marketing reflects a humble acceptance of interdependence. Correcting the errors of capitalism requires a break from brand-shielded anonymity and a refocusing on faces. Can you see them? The people who are building your tractors? Sewing your clothing? Feeding your children's minds? Investing the funds you have entrusted to the bank? There are furry, feathered and scaly faces too, that reflect similar qualities of soul. Nature made it a lot harder to kick one another in the tail when we're looking each other in the eye.

Chapter 2
Pre-planning for sustainable marketing

Preliminary planning may be your most important marketing tool. Careful thought and choice-making at this basic level is the step that most of your competitors will have overlooked when they got started. Ooops! If you did too, don't worry, it is never too late to recover this advantage—just do it now. All of this planning may seem like too much time and energy at first, but it will repay in agreement, direction, confidence, clear assessment and efficiency. A plan primes you for quick action and contingencies. Helen and Scott Nearing shared this reminder in *Living the Good Life*:

> *For all your days prepare.*
> *And meet them ever alike:*
> *When you are the anvil, bear -*
> *When you are the hammer, strike*
> — Edwin Markham

Life isn't simple and neither is honest livelihood; the more carefully integrated the elements of your business planning, the more generously your market actions will meet your needs and values.

Since the patterns of conventional marketing tend to draw us toward profit rather than quality of life or accountability, responsible marketing is virtually impossible without a map outlining where you want to go and how to get there. The planning process itself requires a map: market planning begins with a comprehensive business plan. In farming—a more complex enterprise than the average business—the business plan is properly based on a whole farm plan.

A thoughtful plan will direct the resources you're investing to best advantage. It also generates an attitude of conviction that will compel employees, customers, investors and outlets to take you seriously. According to author Peter Drucker, most new businesses fail. Many that do survive require 7-10 years to become financially successful. Comprehensive planning that accounts for adequate capitalization of your personnel and resources will help you to thrive where other upstarts fall short.

Working through each step is the key. The task is not all dry, and some of it is downright juicy! Because you and your business are unique, creating your own map is imperative; but if you find yourself feeling overwhelmed by all of the uncertainties and possibilities in planning, remember that you are not alone. Seeking assistance when you need it will help you work through the process.

My own difficulty is instructive. Having sold agricultural and value-added products (baked goods, etc.) since I was a kid running our roadside stand, I felt familiar with many aspects of marketing when I began an organic specialty foods business three years ago. Still, experience did not guide me painlessly; in fact, it sent me into paralysis. I was now selling raw and gluten-free prepared foods (breads, cereals and snacks) that appealed to a more specific public and required a different approach. I had ideas—but no clear plan—for providing a quality product in a responsible manner: purchasing as many ingredients as possible from small, local farmers; packaging as simply as possible; focusing on freshness and minimal processing; and marketing regionally in order to cut down on product transportation.

My mother, with whom I had the foresight to go into business, was equally inexpert with planning despite the assurance that experience had earned her. We launched the busi-

Organic marketing grows from realistisc planning and preparation.

ness—Good Stuff by Mom & Me—only to spend two tiresome years regularly wishing that we hadn't. We were so busy tossing on the waves of market demand that it took us a while to realize that we had neglected to really establish a plan for what we wanted to do, where we wanted to go and how we were going to get there.

We had set off with poor bearings, no real goals and few maps: getting lost was the consequence. Getting started is the biggest hurdle to planning. My best advice for finishing your map is to start, then take it step by step:

> *Thirty years ago my older brother, who was ten years old at the time, was trying to get a report on birds written that he'd had three months to write. It was due the next day. We were out at our family cabin in Bolinas, and he was at the kitchen table close to tears, surrounded by binder paper and pencils and unopened books on birds, immobilized by the hugeness of the task ahead. Then my father sat down beside him, put his arm around my brother's shoulder, and said, 'Bird by bird, buddy. Just take it bird by bird'.*
>
> — Anne Lamott, *Bird by Bird: Some Instructions on Writing and Life* 1994

Everything doesn't have to be perfect to get something started. Planning is not a linear process, but approaching it in stages provides the structure for considering things from many angles. Take the time *now* to get your bearings. Think, explore, educate yourself—then do something. Leap as far as your preparation and comfort allows. Remember to keep learning and consciously adjusting your plan as you go. Be like the plants: develop your roots, use all the resources at your disposal. Shun the excuses, give it some time, and remember to look confident along the way.

THE GREATER CONTEXT OF MARKET PLANNING

Here is the overall outline for establishing a successful and sustainable farm-based business, starting with the foundation:

1. Whole Farm Planning
2. Business Planning
3. Market Planning (focus of this Handbook)

Whole farm planning

A comprehensive resource exists for whole farm planning—a companion NOFA Handbook by Elizabeth Henderson and Carl North titled *Whole Farm Planning: Ecological Imperatives, Personal Values and Economics*. It's a tool for envisioning and achieving the foundational requirements for your farm, business and life. Out of this guided introspection a farm-based marketing plan grows naturally. The progression grounds and focuses one's market thinking and avoids reinventing the wheel.

If you do not have access to the Henderson-North handbook, there are a number of other resources available. For an overview of ideas on the subject, do a general search by going to www.Google.com and entering "whole farm planning."

Business planning

One of the best outlines for writing a business plan that I have found is the *NxLeveL™ Guide for Agricultural Entrepreneurs, Tilling the Soil of Opportunity*. The companion class that works through the manual is an excellent way to make valuable contacts while receiving top-notch assistance in the process of developing and implementing your business plan.

The goal here is a comprehensive *written* business plan. This may seem like a real chore at first—it did to me. But when it is all on paper, you are able to refer back to it for direction, assessment and future planning. Plus it is one of your best tools for giving interested and supportive parties—including employees—an understanding of your business structure and goals. Get as many people as possible who have a stake in your business to help in writing it—the more involved your crew feels in the process, the more invested they will be in the plan. Once you have written it, read it over with a critical eye, be sure it makes sense, then move on to making it happen.

A business plan includes the following components:

Executive summary—a detailed description of the business and its principles

Goals & objectives—business concept, mission statement, goals

Background information—industry information (background plus trends), where your business fits

Organizational matters—ownership, business structure, regulation, contacts

Market planning—*coming soon, read on!*

Financial plan—books, records, budget, cash flow

Conclusion—summary, implementation plan

See the pattern? Everything is interconnected, and all this groundwork will support your marketing success. You will know *what* you are doing, *why* and *how*. The business plan itself is a marketing tool. We used ours to "market" the idea of our partnership to my local credit union in order to participate in an Individual Development Account (IDA) savings program that matched the money we saved to expand our small business. These resources allowed Mom & Me to build our own on-site commercial kitchen, a move that improved our efficiency and quality of life, lowered our energy and transportation costs and greatly expanded our market potential.

Market Planning (at last)

Market Planning is the focus of the rest of this Handbook. Exploitive concepts of vast profitability—unlimited growth, unrestricted consumption, private and corporate hegemony and disregard for quality—do not apply here. To repeat: sustainable marketing involves an expanded understanding of prosperity that includes the riches of interconnection, personal responsibility, a sense of place and natural scale. The process is figuring out where (financially *and* generally/vitally) your business is now, determining where you want it to be, and taking it there. If making an abundant and deeply satisfying living is your destination, this process will provide an invaluable tool for planning your route.

You may be surprised how naturally market planning sprouts from the whole farm and business planning process. Building on the goals and realities you have identified, we will explore the field of marketing, available resources, contemporary trends and possibilities—along with some innovative success stories—to help you consider marketing's primary concerns.

We will also consider product presentation and effective action steps: community relations, promotions, advertising, assessment and management.

Remember that the pathways to successful marketing are innumerable. The ones that might work for you are as distinctive as your fingerprints. The landscape is always changing due to new neighbors, the latest health and community concerns, local and international influences, innovation and novel or rediscovered technologies. Prepared action and a habit of observant flexibility will alert you to inviting new pathways and help you avoid dead ends.

Oh. And don't worry that it takes genius to grow a successful business; that result is the reward of good planning, wise counsel, common sense and a willingness to recognize and accept limitations.

Our own story

For two years my mom and I struggled to make ends meet in our business. We worked long hours, expanded our product line, never said no, slept even less and watched our enthusiasm for what we were doing drain out as quickly as our savings account. Our customers were happy, our products sold before we made them, we were appreciated and admired; but though our successes energized us briefly, even these "successes" couldn't keep us going for long.

Looking back, breakdown was inevitable. The end came with a small event at the end of our second summer. We overextended our meager time and resources to cater five days of food for "five hundred pre-registered participants." It was an isolated venue and we were to be one of two food vendors. We prepared for weeks in advance. About two hundred people attended—the organizers had inflated their figures—and we scrambled all week to make it through without losing our shirts and all of our perishable raw materials. We had prepared staples for a capacity crowd, but this small crew clamored for variety and we cranked it out.

People raved; praise and accolades abounded. With pasted smiles and bleary eyes we pressed ourselves and broke even. It was not such a long fall or such a bottomless pit, our falling apart. We made it home and I sank into a week of exhausted gloom and depression. My mom remained dutiful and optimistic, a pleasure for which I deeply resented her. And finally, I gave up. Ready to just throw it in on the whole venture, I grabbed some paper to illustrate why we could not carry on. Instead, in one half hour with pen, paper and calculator, I saw how we could succeed. You can too.

We had started our business tentatively—with a booth at a bi-weekly farmer's market and a trade-show launching of a mail-order program—testing the waters to see what products would sell and who would be interested in buying them. We discovered the Massachusetts Avenue Project, a free shared-use commercial kitchen 45 minutes from our home, and we were able to use their facilities for production and their personnel for assistance in tackling the regulatory process. This worked extremely well for us; retaining our other incomes and without significant overhead, we were able to get a feel for the market without relying upon it.

Our test marketing gave us invaluable insight into what sold well, how to sell it and to whom. The problems began when we got so caught up in producing and managing the day-to-day operation that we neglected to take the time to complete our business and marketing plan. Eventually, we gave up our other incomes and raced around filling every product request— no matter how individualized—with a destructive combination of frantic activity and financial uncertainty.

What's enough? My mom and I may have been producing organic, but we were not marketing sustainably because we were not sustainable! We had taken business classes, listened to all the advice, done a lot of research and even sought out some excellent resources, but we didn't accurately access our resources and financial needs to determine what was enough, so we didn't really know where we were going in terms of profit and business volume. Without these bearings, we were swayed by the promise of immediate profit rather than directed to develop sustained, ongoing revenue.

Beware that road. You will never achieve the undefined goal of "profit" no matter how much you work, how little you sleep, or how terrific your products are. When I sat with my pen and paper, I did only one thing: self-evaluation. By determining *enough*—what we needed to earn to cover our overheads and provide us with comfortable incomes—by articulating our personal goals in the venture and the principles that we wanted to uphold in achieving them—it was easy to see realistic paths to these ends. The turning point for us was that straightforward. We are now both happy and successful in our business. The box [opposite] tells how we got there.

Being so methodical and choosy was incredibly effective for our type of products—shelf-stable organic convenience foods for health-conscious folks—and the level of production that we wanted to engage in. One of our goals was to keep our production small—neither of us wanted to manage a large-scale operation and we both wanted free time to work on other projects. We wanted to provide regular work for some family members without managing other hired labor. We did not want to deal with innumerable individual orders. As stores became regular customers, we began to receive requests from other stores and from customers for personalized orders. It is still hard to say no, but for now we are selling enough.

Sometimes it feels harder to take it slow and define growth than it is to acquiesce to market pressures. Small for us has been a determination of

STEPS TO DO-ABILITY, SUCCESS

My mother and I, working with our calculation of "enough" profit, outlined how many of our best selling products we would need to market to achieve that figure. The numbers were not daunting. From here it was a simple process to identify the most popular products that we could produce efficiently with minimal equipment. We dropped the rest of the products and learned to say no (remember *enough*?) to requests that did not fit our new plan.

Meanwhile, we identified a number of small, regionally-based outlets with high product turnover—mostly mid-sized health food stores and cooperatives in New York State—in areas where we expected our products would be in high demand. We called these stores and asked if they would be interested in receiving a sample of our products (checking the address and contact person) and sent out our most popular item with a packet of information including a personalized letter, information about our business (who we are, what we do), wholesale prices and ordering information. We followed up with a call and received preliminary orders from most of the stores. With the first orders, we sent a display sign and updated ordering information.

quality—in our lives and products—over quantity. Now we have a business and marketing plan. We refer to it for every major decision that faces us and re-evaluate it as our priorities and life needs change. It allows us a focus and flexibility that we never had when we were working with the vague notion that we were never earning quite enough. Now we know what we are doing, why and how.

Chapter 3
Planning issues & analysis

Are you ready? Take pencil and paper in hand to record ideas along the way. In the Market Planning Outline, each main section begins with questions for you to consider and moves on to explore marketing issues relating to the topic. At the end of each section, return to these questions. Brainstorming and non-critically recording your thoughts may be a good way to get started. Eventually, you will want to answer these questions as succinctly as possible in writing. The end result will be a framework for a marketing plan that takes into account a number of important issues. You may want to identify others; this overview will provide methods and insights for identifying your best marketing strategies. *Enjoy the journey!*

Here's the outline of the market planning process—and this chapter—for easy reference:

Sustainable Market Planning

Section 1. Self Analysis

> Principles & Responsibilities
> People & Quality of Life
> Sense of Place
> Natural Limits

Section 2. Community Analysis

> Interconnection
> Circle of Influence
> Synergy & Possibility

Section 3. Market Analysis

> Customer Analysis
> Market Trends & Issues
> Market Size & Potential

Section 4. Marketing Strategies

> Product Strategies
> Price & Quality Issues
> Promotional Strategies
> Placement/Selling Strategies

Section 5. Products and Services

Section 6. Management and Assessment

Our energy and desire are the wings that support us not just in our life's bread labor, but in the spirit of service behind it.

SECTION 1: SELF ANALYSIS

The goal of self analysis is to identify the formative values and realities of your life, quantify the resources available to you and outline your ideal business parameters.

Self-analysis involves an exploration of the nature of your life, looking to your needs and values to determine your own personal business blueprint. Like the example below, your outline may include the intermeshing of numerous ventures, work on or off the farm, or any number of combinations of possibilities. This is *your* personal (or family) plan. It should look very much like you.

Example: Anatole North, from Van Etten, N.Y., builds his life around the principle of simplicity. A farmer, artist and carpenter, he struggled to create an income that embodied the limited reliance on fossil fuels, power tools and toxic materials that he desired. He wanted to spend his time working with plants and creating beautiful and useful works of art but was not certain he could make a living doing that. His solution? He significantly pared down his need for cash by growing the majority of his food in a home garden and began a business crafting high-end wood bowls from local woods with traditional hand tools. He has cut back his carpentry work as his business has grown and he has found local machine-free landscaping work to supplement his income.

Principles and responsibilities

Sustainable marketing is the result of business practices founded on principles of nature—self-renewal through completed cycles and no waste, modest resource use...a lifelike balance of cooperation and competition, taking, giving and leaving alone, etc. This aspect of self analysis involves exploring these ideas at a personal level. If you are involved in a group venture, have as many members as possible respond personally before working towards a group response. The following questions may help us to identify the principles and responsibilities that your business will embody.

- What are your underlying principles and goals?
- What is important to you?
- What do you feel responsible for?

Your principles are part of the foundation for your business

Underlying marketing (and life) actions is an inner-to-outer progression that goes something like this:

1. Motivations and principles—Our underlying structure of desires and beliefs provides the energy and guidance for our actions.

2. Imagination—Based on our motivations and principles we picture possible action plans.

3. Vision—Something strong takes shape from the possibilities.

4. Goals—We begin to think in real time and resources, establish parameters and objectives for our action steps.

5. Actions—We act to reach our goals in the manner and time we planned.

Upon our principles and motivations—positive or negative, ethical or unethical, examined or overlooked—we found marketing actions that foster harmony or dysfunction. The folks who will support your business make decisions in a similar manner. Letting them know what motivates your business actions is a powerful way to achieve specific goals that will forward your ideals while helping you to win (and keep) customers. Tell your customers what you believe in—post signs, outline your motivation in stories or newsletters. Give your community a chance to support principles that they believe in by letting them know how you translate your beliefs into action.

Here are some examples of principle in action:

PRINCIPLE	RESPONSIBILITY/GOAL	MARKET ACTION
Interconnection	Cherish the natural order	Respect your customers
Interdependence	Nurture people, environment	Utilize sustainable methods
Quality	Social/environmental justice	Sell ethically produced products
Natural limits	Determine and live "enough"	Limit pursuit of profit
Responsibility	Respect the integrity of the commons	Engage in honest, directed sales promotion

Determining your areas of influence and responsibility

With all this focus on responsibility, remember, also, that there are limits to what you are responsible for. Your circle of influence defines those areas in which you can take action—interactions for which you are directly responsible. Beyond this lies your circle of concern. The only way to effect change in the external circle is to manifest your concerns internally and act upon them. Such action is also one of your most effective marketing tools. Building your marketing plan on this proactive principle will develop the focus and efficiency that are the foundations of business success.

People & quality of life

Examine who you are—what you desire most in life, what you have energy for, what you don't. Explore the reality of where you are right now, what skills and resources you possess, what and whom you know, how you enjoy spending your time, how you *don't* want to spend it. When you determine your livelihood, you're defining much of what your life is going to consist of. To outline your ideal, and then the reality of your situation today, will help you to see where you are and where you may want to go.

- Who are you? What issues are important to your quality of life?
- What do you want your life experience to be?
- What are your skills, interests, concerns; what satisfies and motivates you?

> *I am one*
> *Who eats his breakfast,*
> *   Gazing at the morning-glories*
> *   — Basho*

If you are like Basho, you may not want to create a livelihood that denies you the pleasure of morning reflection. It is sometimes hard to draw the line between your life and your business, and customers tend to see these things as one and the same, too. Make no mistake about it, when you market your products, you are marketing yourself. What sells? Enthusiasm, competence, happiness, engagement, joy, dedication, harmony... You have got to be in the right business if you want to be successful in sustainable marketing. Understanding your talents and temperament and getting to know those of the people you are working with are the foundation for building your marketing plan and ensuring that you are doing what you *enjoy*. Believe it or not, that is what really sells. With a bit of creativity, even the most soul-nourishing objectives can find their way into action in a business plan.

Sense of place—location

Identify and examine your production and sales locations. This provides the external parameters upon which to base your marketing decisions.

- Where will you produce your products?
- Where will you sell your products?
- What are the opportunities and needs in this place?

Know your whereabouts. An important factor in determining what to produce and how to sell it is where you are. Successful marketing is always a function of the conditions at hand. When assessing an exciting plan that has been profitable for someone else, consider the conditions of their location. Are they similar to yours? If not, can the concept be adapted to fit the realities of your situation? Here are some things to consider:

- Are there established markets within a workable distance?
  Explore local area for opportunities such as farmers markets, restaurants, cooperatives and institutions.
- Can you take advantage of mail-order markets for fresh or value-added products?
- Are there organizations and infrastructure already available that could be utilized?
  Researching local resources could save you a great deal of time and effort, reveal market possibilities, suggest a new line with limited investments of time or money, and lead to invaluable business assistance. Examples of resources available to Northeast farmers include: the Farm to Chef initiative in Vermont, Farm to School programs in several states, shared-use commercial kitchens and processing facilities.
- Is this a prime location for anything in particular? What could I

do successfully here?

Soil conditions, climate, availability of water, historical land use and what's currently established are clues to what your area is suited for.

- What is MISSING here? What do people need?
  What's in demand will provide guidance for your market offerings. Possibilities include community supported agriculture, market or farm stands, special niches and value-added products.

Natural limits—enough

Determine your real financial needs. Define "enough" to establish an honest and considered target for profit.

- What are your fixed and what are your more flexible monetary needs?
- What is a reasonable profit?
- What is enough?

Working with what is finite and mutual. We live with the reality that our resource base is both finite and common. Yet neither market analysis nor behavior reflects an understanding of the ultimate consequences of unchecked consumption.

> *As consumers, we are often unaware of the direct link between our demand for material goods and services and the need to extract and process additional natural resources from the environment... We often ignore the undeniable fact that most environmental problems can be traced directly to our own consumption, and that our consumption is someone else's pollution.*

> — Hall et al, *Energy & Resource Quality*

Not only does nature have limits for production, the market has limits for earnings. This may be where exploitive marketing fosters the most profound breakdown in our common abundance. If you do not establish reasonable limits for your earnings, you will end up putting in a lot more effort than necessary and removing that potential for someone else. As unorthodox as such thinking is in the greater culture, many of us find there are riches in practicing contentment.

What do I need? must be among the first questions in approaching your market plan. The determination involves a realistic assessment of the current state of your life and business, a definition of reasonable profit and a means of assessing and preparing for future needs. This is *not* about relegating yourself to a life of poverty. It is about establishing a baseline and a plan for manifesting a level and quality of prosperity in your life that is, by conscious intent, in harmony with the world at large.

This was it—the saving grace of my own business. When we finally took the time out of our harried schedule to figure out what was enough, we were also able to see how we could earn it with a lot less effort. A friend of mine is a rock-climbing guide. When a climber gets in a tough spot with no evident hand or footholds in sight, she tells them to *stretch*: Any new perspective—even 1/4 inch—is enough to open up a whole new world of opportunity. This new perspective gave us our lives back. It was the key to our marketing success: the ability to stay in business.

Everyone will have a different assessment of "enough." We began by taking a close look at our personal finances and identifying a figure that supported maintenance (rent/mortgage, food, heat, transport, taxes etc.), emergency savings, retirement savings, expenses (gifts, entertainment, travel etc.), education and charity. Then we did a similar evaluation of the business. Here is a general equation to help you quantify "enough":

Enough income =

fixed needs + reasonable profit + future needs – resources available

There are many excellent budgeting and assessment tools out there for determining how to work with the above figures. One good place to start is www.nxlevel.org. NOFA's *Whole Farm Planning* Handbook (Henderson & North, 2004) also provides tools for current and future needs assessment and suggestions for finding "social capital" that may translate into funding for your enterprise. As for what your business needs, it is important to seek out wise counsel in your decision-making process. As we will discuss later, many conventional "needs" like expensive blanket advertising are not necessary in sustainable marketing. Assess your needs. Are they *real*?

Enough already? Not quite. Limits seem to exist in every aspect of life. Back in 322 BC Aristotle philosophized:

> *Most people think that a state in order to be happy ought to be large; but even if they are right, they have no idea of what is a large and what a small state… To the size of states there is a limit, as there is to other things, plants, animals, implements; for none of these retain their natural power when they are too large or too small, but they either wholly lose their nature, or are spoiled.*

Science appears to be in agreement: there may even be precise specs for the scale of successful communities. This may seem to be an arbitrary concern in marketing, but as you will see, it is not. British Anthropologist Robin Dunbar has observed that in all species of primate—every variety of monkey and ape—the larger the neocortex of their brain, the larger the average size of the groups they live with. He theorizes that a species' brain size is an important factor in their ability to handle the intricacies of larger social groups. Extrapolating the significant additional social and intellectual burdens of even small increases in the size of a group, he has determined that "the figure of 150 seems to represent the maximum number of individuals with whom [humans] can have a genuinely social relationship, the kind of relationship that goes with knowing who they are and how they relate to us." Scouring anthropological literature, he repeatedly encountered operational entities of this size in historic societal, military and religious units, leading him to observe that "planners have discovered, by trial and error over the centuries, that it is hard to get more than this number of men sufficiently familiar with each other so that they can work together as a functional unit." Something to keep in mind in creating your business and marketing communities.

It is interesting to note that at least one business—Gore, the producers of Gore-Tex—has modeled its operation on this concept. The corporation has received ample recognition for employee satisfaction. They have no management hierarchy. Each unit is made up of 150 people; when a unit grows larger they split off some aspect of the production and move it to another building. In another departure from the corporate norm, within each unit is every skill necessary to bring a product from conception to sales. Peer responsibility—rather than managerial oversight—drives performance. The company is highly successful. They also claim that when the units have been allowed to grow much larger, performance has suffered. community supported agriculture (CSA) farms and other enterprises that would benefit from community formation may find this example informative. The fascinating thing about respecting limits is that being in harmony with them actually supports your potential for business success by decreasing the pressures against you. You could work harder if you wanted to, but why?

SECTION 2: COMMUNITY RELATIONS ANALYSIS

The goal of community relations analysis is to take a close look at the community in which your business exists and envision the relations it will develop with that public.

Example: Gail Thorpe and her family, from East Aurora, N.Y, have designed their farm marketing to reflect the spiritual and community values that govern their lives. Basing their market practices on faith, charity and trust, they have been able to keep their prices reasonable and their offerings generous (including a policy of "taking what you need," and a number of unlimited "pick-your-own" and canning/freezing bulk discounts). They offer a free yearly CSA membership to families in need and encourage other members to assist in this support. This commitment to service has enabled mid- and low-income individuals to join the farm's market community. Ruth Bindig, mother of four, has just signed up for her second year in the CSA. She has been looking forward to the first distribution and the variety of fruits and vegetables that her share brings to her family's meals. In the off-season she is rarely able to afford the higher prices of supermarket organics. Now her kids help her to pick and preserve food for the winter. Reconnecting her family with their food source and their neighbors makes them all feel like a part of something special.

Interconnection:
Staff development & connection marketing

Clearly identify your partners, staff and customers; consider ways to optimize your interactions with them and their interactions with one another.

- Who are your customers? Your communities?
- How will you assess and choose your staff members?
- How can you connect your customers to one another and to your business and products?

The value of connection. The Dalai Lama maintains that engaging in interactions that support others increases our sense of peace and wellbeing. This observation has been echoed throughout the ages and provides invaluable insight for life and marketing: what we do to help others ends up benefiting—even sustaining—ourselves. Successful marketing, like community, is the result of relationships based on kindness and human connection. Standardized supermarkets and department stores stock and sell with as little human contact as possible. Employees are replaced with automated checkout machines. The corporation relies on the familiarity of advertisement and brand confidence to simulate community and convince us of value. Here it's ambiguous who is responsible and we are left feeling no one is really accountable for things like employee rights and social and environmental concerns.

Small business places a premium on quality relationships. The attitudes that you foster at the top spread through your business, infecting family members, employees and customers. People are interacting with people again. Your customers see and hear how you treat one another within your business structure; they experience it in the attention they receive from you and your employees. Their regard for these exchanges is reflected in their eagerness to support your business efforts with their patronage. Satisfied customers and employees often become your best friends and promotional agents. Can you picture the following scenario at your local Wal-Mart?

> *What kind of new human bonds are established? At our farm, I think back to the drought of 1999. Worst drought in 100 years...a truly brutal growing season. And we irrigated everything, constantly. The strain on the farmers did not go unnoticed by our customers. By early July, customers started asking us, "Are you guys OK?" A few had tears in their eyes. "Do you want to just forget it? Keep the money, and we'll do it again next year?" Such compassion brought tears to our eyes. We couldn't believe it. We thanked everyone for their concern, and reassured them that, despite the horrid weather, things would be fine. They were and we finished out the year.*

—George DeVault, Pheasant Hill Farm Emmaus, Pa.

The female influence. According to Faith Popcorn—a top forecaster of consumer trends and advisor to many Fortune 500 companies—women are the dominant economic force in this country, controlling 80 per cent of household spending, and their influence is bringing interconnection to the marketplace. Agriculture echoes this trend. Carolyn Sachs, professor of rural sociology at Penn State, reports that women are major operators—primary or full agricultural partners—on 53 per cent of farms. A growing number of women in the Northeast are involved in agriculture for local urban sales.

Both Popcorn and Sachs assert that women do things differently, that women's farms tend to be smaller, with little need for heavy mechanical equipment and low capital demand. In the marketplace, they say, women tend to assess products and make purchases based on different criteria than men—and traditional marketing techniques. Placing a high priority on human interactions, women seek to build and maintain relationships. Popcorn's number one guide for marketing to women is:

Connecting your customers to each other
connects them to your product

Marketing expert Lori Moskowitz Lepler claims that women are three times more likely than men to recommend a specific brand or producer to friends seeking a particular product or service. Women connect and network, and the more this interconnection involves your products or services, the more people—and business—will be channeled to your enterprise.

Oprah Winfry's story is a testament to the strength of connection marketing. Oprah's achievement—one of the largest media successes in history—is based on connecting women to one another through "universal goals and interests" like self-improvement. What worked in media is instructive to farm marketing. Few enterprises are more uniquely suited to nurturing value-based connection than a small to mid-sized organic farm where a local, owner-on-premises venture fosters relationships between people via accessibility, regular contact, personality galore...in the process supporting clean food and healthful production practices.

CSA farms are a perfect example of creating a community of customers. Such an enterprise can facilitate any number of connections: group pickups at member houses in the neighborhood, volunteer or member workdays (projects like planting garlic), and seasonal picnics. Any event or avenue that brings your customers together—farm days, harvest dinners, recipe "chat" rooms on-line, volunteer work days—is an opening for creating a community that will support your marketing efforts. Few things provide as perfect an opportunity for patron satisfaction as connecting over good food!

Farmers markets are another natural opportunity for powerful community connection, and the number of local markets has exploded in the last decade as more people on both sides of the booth are looking for sustainability and social justice in agriculture. Connection points here are innumerable: fresher, tastier foods; renewed human contact; support of our neighbors and local economies; and reduced fossil fuel consumption transporting distant foods to local tables.

Connection marketing describes this style of doing business. Its real strength is in the sense of belonging that it engenders. So, if you can't meet your customers face to face, then find other ways to engage them. This idea goes back to the earliest days of advertising, with inventions such as Betty Crocker connecting women to one another through the promotion of an image of a corps of homemakers relying on the benevolent spokeswoman's advice, recipes and suggestions for convenience and support. Whatever ways you can think of to connect your customers to one another and the values of your enterprise will increase their loyalty and support.

The Farmer's Diner in Barre, Vt. is a great example of connection marketing. Serving up a full menu of locally grown and produced foods, the diner promotes regional consumption by connecting patrons to the farmers who grew their meal. By including producers' names with their products, displaying pictures of farms and farmland and telling the personal stories behind the images, the diner invites its guests to participate in the story, to be filled and sustained by it and to rediscover the local food system and their integral part in it. The result is a sense that eating at the Farmers' Diner is doing something worthwhile, which provides a strong incentive to return.

Staffing and customer service—making the connection: Connection marketing is based on trust and sustained goodwill. It requires that you treat your staff—your active connection to your customers—as your most important asset. The interactions that they engage in will be the making or breaking of your business; a comprehensive customer service focus is a marketing imperative.

One of the most innovative unions of staffing and customer service policies that I have come across is from The Inn at Little Washington, voted as "America's Best" in Zagat 2003. Chef Patrick O'Connell discussed the Inn's ongoing success in a recent interview:

> *These days, it's often said every company is in the service industry. That requires a shift in your staff's mentality: all of these policies help convey to our people that they don't deal in financial transactions, but rather financial dependencies—we owe our business to the customer and great service comes from showing incredible gratitude for precisely that.*

The Inn at Little Washington is famous for appreciating its customers. They take this practice so seriously that they have created a five-course system for "delivering the perfect experience." It is a meal worth serving no matter what business you're in. Much of their success stems from the amazing way they cultivate their employees. Managing with direction, clarity of expectation, challenge, reward and follow through, this inn has managed to achieve a virtually unheard of employee retention rate in an industry that is known for endless turnover. With accolades from customers, employees and critics, theirs is an approach worth considering.

The Inn at Little Washington's outline for success:

Measure the customer's mood—*Goal #1: showing the customer that you care.* When a new party arrives they are assigned a mood rating from 1-10 (low to high), it is written on the order and the whole staff makes it their business to be certain that they leave with a mood rating of 9 or higher.

Cultivate expertise—*Goal #2: knowing what controls the marketplace and the perceptions of your customers.* All staff members are assigned research projects from studying restaurant reviews to becoming resident experts on a particular subject—like mushrooms—and presenting it to the rest of the staff members. Active learning is expected of every employee.

Tolerate failure...once—*Goal #3: impeccable follow-through.* Practicing "instant correction" reduces employee anxiety by letting them know what is expected and not allowing bad habits to form. Expecting quality work, and holding employees accountable, assures a high level of performance.

Hire for attitude—*Goal #4: cultivating a staff with the desire to please.* This is where the inn does something I have never seen before. They have found that applicants who have positive things to say about their previous jobs make better employees. They hire on this basis rather than technical ability or experience, finding that "over time, nice people can be taught almost anything." Interesting. And it works.

Don't say no (or even I don't know)—*Goal #5: educating the staff.* If a guest asks, for example, if an appetizer is sweet, a waiter will not answer "no" (they are not allowed to say it ever, under any circumstances)—even if it is incredibly spicy—instead the server will describe it thoroughly and let customers decide for themselves. Waiters must pass a rigorous test in which veteran staffers ask them every conceivable question about the inn before they are eligible for a full cut of the large tip pool. They even circulate a monthly newsletter and a list of most asked questions to keep everyone up to date.

Circle of influence:
Assessing *real* value

Consider your effects on the commons and the real value of your products and services.

- What is your circle of influence?
- What is unique about your business?
- What are the needs that your business is addressing?

What do they need? Circle of influence refers to the commons that you directly share with those in your town or region. A comprehensive review of your effects in this area includes an honest assessment of your use of shared resources and all aspects of your interface with the world:

waste generation, media management, employee policies, purchasing, shipping, energy use and the like. As farm-based businesses often demand a relatively localized market, it's impossible to overstate the importance of a marketing campaign based on meeting the needs—through product offerings, customer service and communications—of the people in your sales area.

Even your choice of products and services to offer carries a community responsibility. Do you remember the story of Dr. Seuss's famous exploiter the Once-ler? He had terrific marketing savvy, but no sense of community responsibility:

> The Lorax said, "Sir! You are crazy with greed.
> There is no one on earth who would buy that fool Thneed!"
> But the very next minute I proved he was wrong.
> For, just at that minute, a chap came along,
> and he thought that the Thneed I had knitted was great.
> He happily bought it for three ninety-eight.
> I laughed at the Lorax, "You poor stupid guy!
> You never can tell what some people will buy."

A more nurturing approach is to get to know your neighbors and what is happening in your community in order to understand need and possibilities. This involves pinpointing (rather than creating) unmet needs; and recognizing the local resources, counsel and infrastructure available to assist you in meeting them. The important thing to remember is that responsible marketing begins with responsible products; take the time to identify the real needs of your customers first, and offer products judiciously. Mainstream capitalism (which the Once-ler practices) may use scantily clad women in ads to sell beer, but the "commodity" they are selling is sex. Perceived benefits like this readily morph into perceived need—they drive desire and sell people products that they do not really need.

The responsibility for overconsumption falls as much on those who bring products to market—and prey on human instinct—as on as those who make the purchases. One way to make a responsible judgment as a marketer is to weigh your potential gains from the sale of an item with the social and environmental costs of selling it. If I were to perform this consideration on soda, for instance, here is how I would begin to assess the real value of my product:

Economics: In 1997 Americans spent more than $54 billion on 14 billion gallons of soft drink. People appear to be willing to spend money on soda.

Market demand: Babies are weaned onto soda pop—a fifth of one- and two-year-olds drink a cup a day. The average teenage boy downs 19 ounces daily—more than a can and a half. There is ample market demand for soda if the market is not saturated.

Perceived benefit: Soda is marketed as "refreshing," "satisfying" and "cool." Demand for high-image brands indicates that marketing is effective—customers are buying this image.

Social effects: Some 12 per cent of boys and 11 per cent of girls are obese. In the past 20 years, obesity levels in adolescents have tripled. The World Health Organization has implicated soft drinks and other high sugar drinks in obesity, dental decay, diabetes and other serious health concerns. Soda will raise the burden on health care services and add to individual suffering while providing no real social benefits that I can think of.

Environmental effects: Lots of packaging, chemical additives. No benefits.

Actual need: None. There are many more beneficial ways to hydrate and take in calories.

Real value: Though they may have profit potential, soft drinks bring few real benefits—and many detriments—to individual and common wellbeing. If I think beyond the bottom line, my values and assessments would not allow me to feel good about producing and selling soda. Your value assessment may look different than mine, but it is important to think about the question. It may seem superfluous in your farm business but it is fundamental. Such considerations might have warded off factory farming, hormone-induced dairy production, transgenic introductions, and just about every other issue that people in the organic movement protest. Study real needs and sell beneficials—not a fantasy.

Synergy: Customer service, staff development, conflict resolution & communication

Consider how you will develop your staff, resolve conflict and develop effective communication on all levels of your business. Outline your customer service policy.

- How can you approach staff management to optimize customer service, effective communications and conflict resolution?
- What is your customer service policy?
- How can you create a win-win synergy between your business and customers/staff in conducting your marketing operations?

Be humble; communicate. Tensions from ineffective communication and unresolved conflict can undermine working and market relationships. Managing your business will inevitably lead to a certain amount of conflict. The way you deal with it will make or break your business and affect the loyalty of your customers. One marketing study estimates that companies can almost double their profits by retaining just five per cent more of their customers; another estimates that it costs four to six times more to convert a customer than to retain one. Humility is the key to conflict resolution with customers. In business, there is little room for arrogance or an inflated sense of self-importance. Being able to transform your pride into careful listening and remembering your long-term goals are elements of conflict management and are essential to effective marketing.

The Dalai Lama gives us a clear image of anger to consider:

> *We can conceive of the nature of mind in terms of the water in a lake. When the water is stirred up by a storm, the mud from the lake's bottom clouds it, making it appear opaque. But the nature of the water is not dirty. When the storm passes, the mud settles and the water is left clear once again.*

In the marketplace, we want the water—and the atmosphere—to remain as clear and inviting as possible. Your goal is to surround your products and image with positivity and good will—these are the qualities that pay sustaining dividends. To minimize the inevitable strains, it is important to proactively establish distinct written goals for conflict management with written policies for staff members and for customers. As your employees may well be on the front line dealing with your customers, it is important that you have clear customer service policies.

Customer service

We have probably all heard Stew Leonard's customer service directive: "Rule One is that the customer is always right. Rule Two is that if the customer is wrong, see Rule One." Forward-thinking customer and employee service plans have transformed this three-store Connecticut-New York dairy-grocery into one of the most successful markets in the country. Stew Leonard's takes their commitment to customer service so seriously that they actually run training seminars on the subject to help other companies learn how: www.stewleonards.com (800 729-9692).

There is tremendous power in a strong foundation of customer service. Customers *are* your business. The social side of shopping is about wanting to be treated well. Consumer studies find again and again that the most common reasons customers abandon stores and service providers is that they feel they have been poorly treated. When the customer wins, you win more than just their business, but also the good word that they will share about your business.

Staff relations and management

Stew Leonard, Jr., President and CEO of Stew Leonard's, gives us further insight into the store's success: "Growing up and working in our original dairy store, my father always told me 'You can't have a great place to shop without it first being a great place to work'." Their employee policies have proven so effective that the business is routinely listed amongst Fortune 500's top 100 companies to work for. Stew Leonard attributes this success to having clear policies and expectations for all employees, prioritizing staff development and incentive programs and creating a fun and supportive workplace. Individual commitment to the overall goals is enhanced by the practice of involving everyone in the creation of team goals that are specific and easy to work with. For instance, they break their overall philosophy down into "S.T.E.W.": "Satisfy the customer; Teamwork gets it done; Excellence makes it better; WOW makes it fun."

Effective communication

Even the most comprehensive staff and customer service policies will not sidestep conflict altogether, so it is important to be prepared to deal with it in a constructive way. To some extent or other, we all fall into the trap of assuming that "everyone is like me"; it is easy to develop an image of a "right" or "normal" way of being as we rely on our own experience to understand others and their motivations. The hard truth is that people really are different; wearing different filters of experience and armed with different tools of assessment. We do not see the world as the world is, but as *we are*—while believing we see things objectively. Embracing the limits of our own views requires modesty. It is the radical first step in successful communication and conflict negotiation.

Incidentally, your way of looking at the world is by no means just a stumbling block; it is also a relationship and marketing tool. You, in your authenticity, are in a unique position to attract and influence people—not only those you know but also those whose interests and concerns resemble yours.

Communication is the bridge between you and your associates, staff, customers. The quality of that bridge will determine how solidly you connect. Effective communication is a process. It progresses from listening to developing an understanding and then speaking. Communication starts with your ears.

Effective marketing communications must be explicit. When you are prepared to speak yourself, there is a timeworn method for getting your point across that can apply to staff directives, promotional materials, written or spoken information:

> Tell the audience what you are going to tell them.
> Tell them.
> Tell them what you told them.

You cannot depend on common sense to take your customers and staff where you want them to go. Sometimes they will do the opposite of what you planned, and make assumptions that you could never have imagined. The more information reinforcement you can provide, the clearer people will be for why they support you as a satisfied employee or by buy your products rather than going to the supermarket.

Conflict management

Steven Covey offers the following analysis of conflict resolution for effective business management decisions:

Outcome	Power Structure	Benefit Equation
Win-Win	Creation, Mutual Benefit	$1+1=3$
No Deal	Agree to Disagree	$1, 1$
Compromise	Acceptable	$1+1=2$
Lose-Win	Martyrdom	$0+1=1$
Win-Lose	Authoritarianism	$1+0=1$

The most appealing outcome of a conflict is mutual benefit: Win-Win. This is not the easy, nice choice (that might be martyrdom), it is the courageous choice: a balance between self-respect and respect for others. Such mutual benefit is the key to Stew Leonard's "customer is always right" philosophy.

The way you approach conflict management is a marketing opportunity. You have a greater stake in this than either your employees or customers do. To approach resolution with a clear head and an open mind, do not bring anger to work. Anger destroys our critical faculties, and the angrier we are, the more people instinctively shun us.

SECTION 3: MARKET ANALYSIS

The goal of market analysis is an understanding of the marketplace in which your business is operating. It involves researching your market scope, available counsel and resources, and business possibilities and challenges.

Example: Laulima Farm on the island of Maui in Hawaii could not have much to complain about, could they? But the community supported agriculture (CSA) farm struggled to distribute weekly boxes of produce to their members. Taking a close look at the needs of their community, it became clear that there was demand not only for fresh, local produce, but also for a neighborhood gathering spot and snack shop. Using local materials, the farm crew built an inviting roadside hut and began selling produce and value-added treats like smoothies. The stand is now a popular hangout and the major outlet for the farm's products.

Customer analysis:
Researching your market

Precisely determine who your customers are, what they want and need, what their habits are and how you can reach them with your marketing efforts.

Who is my target market? What do my customers want and need?
What is my competitive advantage? What is the best positioning for
my product and its promotion?
Who are my counselors? Where can I find the information that I
need?

"Choosing" your customers. As you determine your market scope, keep in mind that you have a lot of latitude to determine who your customers will be—the more familiar you are with the customers in your target audience, the more likely you are to succeed. Market to a clientele that you like, respect and are comfortable with. Target people who need what you want to sell, are accessible to you, and have a reason to buy from you instead of someone else. Look for benefits that you can provide your customers: closer to home, more pick-up dates, more convenient locations, higher quality.

Successful marketing relies on an effective synthesis of your knowledge of the results of directed research and the courage and ability to make decisions based on incomplete knowledge. The underlying goal of research and analysis is to determine market potential by taking into account not just the facts, but also the opinions that give definition to the facts regarding product potential, customer profiles and needs.

The first goal of marketing research is to understand customer pur-

Know your customers: their demographics (gender, age, family status, ethnic origin, etc.) and what they think about and care about.

chase behavior with specific answers to the questions:

> Who are my target customers?
>
> What are their demographics: gender, age, income, occupation, location, family status, children, education, ethnic origin?
>
> What is the market structure of my customer base: individual customers, retail markets, processors, restaurants?
>
> What are their priorities and expectations? What do they think about?
>
> What are the issues that concern them: health, environment, animal rights, social justice?
>
> How are they thinking about these issues: aspirations, concerns, prevailing thoughts and trends, local politics?
>
> What sources are available to research these issues: newspapers, magazines, food & agriculture policy websites, scientific find-

ings & reviews, statistical reports, observation, discussion, questionnaires?

Where & how can I reach them with my products and directed advertising?

How will I place my products: farmers markets, cooperatives, mail order, CSA, eating establishments, institutions?

How can I effectively attract customers to my products: promotion, connection, education, invitation?

What do they buy? What are they interested in buying?

What motivates their purchasing decisions: Quality, price, local, organic, natural, unprocessed, convenience, recognition?

How to research market issues

There are many different ways to conduct market research. Whatever way you choose, be sure to take notes and keep track of what you are learning. Here are some of the issues that you will want to research:

- products to offer
- prices the market will support
- quality of similar products available
- selection/diversity to offer
- customer service and reliability available through like businesses
- niches for expertise
- developing a positive reputation
- characteristics of successful business models—location, layout, appearance, sales method, credit policy, availability of products, management, longevity and stability, advertising/promotion and image

Interpersonal, interactive methods. The methods below have the benefit of providing you with immediate information, spontaneous observation and experiential learning:

Work in or manage a business like the one you plan to create

Visit similar businesses, take tours, call to set up personal visits

Talk with people in the line of business you are considering, make lists of questions and write down the answers:

- What kind of problems do you encounter?
- What marketing techniques have been successful for you?
- What are the trends, futures that you see?

Ask people with good judgment in different fields what they see happening in your area.

Visit local business, education and non-profit institutions for information

Keep your eyes open. Isaac Newton claimed: "If I have ever made any valuable discoveries, it has been owing more to patient attention than to any other talent." Give yourself the time to benefit from patient attention in researching and developing a successful business model. Read industry journals, books, newspapers and promotional materials. Observe in real life, search the Internet, attend lectures & conferences.

Market trends & issues

Identify the major trends affecting your market and how these affect your market potential.

- What are the trends that affect my business and market potential?
- What do I need to know to be successful in a changing market-place?
- How have prevailing trends affected businesses like mine?

Healthy skepticism: When researching market trends, remember not to take the projections as the gospel truth—there is a lot of educated guessing going on here. Weigh what you read in industry journals with what you read in mainstream media and process everything back through the screen of your own understanding of how the world works. Glancing through the projections of years past will give you a good feel for how wrong the forecasts can be. The Chicago Tribune's top twenty food trends of 2002 included this bit of ill-advised optimism: "Do not expect to see mad cow infiltrate the U.S. market, according to a study by Harvard University's school of public health." Ah, well. Don't get caught up so much in research that you forget to get your business started; learning is an ongoing process.

Some major values, issues affecting organic farm marketing

Conscience

People are becoming disillusioned with corporate corruption. Companies that have capitalized on "having a conscience" include Ben & Jerry's, Patagonia, & Celestial Seasonings. Having a conscience is what your business is all about. Be vocal, create community, promote all the reasons people can justly feel good about purchasing your products.

Convenience

According to the NDP Group, a research group that tracks consumers' eating habits, the number of people eating breakfast on the run has doubled since 1990. Time is one of a customer's most precious assets. People want to save time shopping and preparing food: helping them do so is one way to expand your market. Opportunities abound for high-quality value-added and ready to eat convenience foods. One idea ripe and ready for small organic farmers is freeze-drying of local organic foodstuffs like chopped fruits and vegetables and prepared sauces and meal options. New technologies and vacuum packing make this an accessible (and virtually untapped) market for local and institutional vendors—perhaps a mechanism for extending seasonal CSAs.

"Live issue" foods

We are living in the information age, new awareness leads to new opportunities. There is a growing interest in "local," "grass-fed," "free-range" foods. The key to encouraging these movements is aggressive education of your customers regarding issues and benefits of your products. Influential buzz words these days include: Drug-free, clean, environmental, fresh, local, humane, traditional, whole foods.

Environment

According to Earth Pledge, more than 2.3 billion pounds of pesticides are used on U.S. farms each year. An average American consumes small amounts of about 20 different pesticides daily in our food and water. More and more people are realizing they have a personal stake in preserving the environment for future generations. They feel good doing something positive for the environment or consuming something that is supposed to be free from pollutants and minimally packaged.

Ethnicity

There are many different ethnic communities in the US—who are the predominant groups in your area? What are their particular needs for products and services? People all over are eating more ethnic foods than they have in the past.

Nutrition

World Health Report 2002 ranked the low intake of fruit and vegetables among the top 10 risk factors contributing to mortality. In 2003 the UN Food and Agricultural Organisation and World Health Organization launched a global campaign recommending that all people eat 400g (14 oz.) of fruit and vegetables each day. What people believe they should eat and what they actually do eat are not necessarily the same. Mixed messages abound. Labeling and nutritional claims—the proliferation of seemingly contradictory information—are one issue, another is cynicism. Despite skepticism and confusion, people still make many purchases based on health claims.

Organic standards

In 1977 NOFA (Vermont & New Hampshire) founded an organic certification program for its members. Since the early 1990s, organics has

become the fastest growing segment of the food industry. The sale of organic food has increased by 20 per cent per year for the past 10 years. Last year, the food industry sold $11 billion worth of organic products. While this is still only a fraction of the overall sales, it has been enough to encourage commercial giants—following

Trends in nutrition and food categories, ethnic and local tastes and other parameters of eating are moving toward the sustainable and organic marketer and present opportunities for the alert entrepreneur.

the letter of the law as outlined by newly instituted National Organic Standards—to enter the field. Upholding the regulatory ecological issues—without addressing issues of scale, the cultural and economic fabric of communities or the imperative for social justice upon which the movement was also founded—has allowed the big guys to undermine smaller-scale producers in the marketplace. In order to address these larger concerns, NOFA-NY (www.nofany.org) developed The Farmers' Pledge [next page], a written commitment to principles beyond the scope of the National Standards. It communicates the essence of responsibility that this Handbook is all about.

The pledge is not a substitute for certification—both are valuable marketing tools for organic farmers—and both are ways to increase customer confidence in your commitment to high quality and integrity. Get certified (if you can afford it) and/or take the pledge. Be sure to post these principles and promote them to your customers.

NOTE: Certification requires a lot of organized record keeping and can be expensive for small operations. It is especially important for selling to stores, perhaps less so if you have a CSA or direct sale market; many restaurants are more interested in high quality "local" foods than "certified" organic.

Public health

The news at the time of this writing has been full of reports of animal-borne illness: mad cow disease and avian flu are producing—thus far—a relatively minor consumer response. However, this is an opportunity that is brewing. It is only a matter of time until we see further breakdown in market confidence for factory farmed meat and dairy products.

Resource security

As a shrinking and unstable global oil supply sends gasoline prices veering to over two dollars per gallon, more people are calling into question the wisdom of relying on food that has been shipped across the country or around the world. Producing, selling and buying local food have all entered a growth cycle. Pennsylvania farmer George DeVault calls this "the best way I know to provide 'homeland security'." I think he is right.

Urban society

Here are the trends we are dealing with in farming and food marketing; In a shockingly short time we have gone from a highly agrarian, food producing society—in 1900 40 per cent of the population lived on farms—to a food purchasing society in which less than 2 per cent of today's population live on farms. Just since 1960, the number of farms has declined from about 3.2 million to 1.9 million while average farm size has increased by 40 per cent. Possibilities for agrotourism and urban fresh markets are growing. Agricultural economist Kelso Wessel sees big opportunity for farmers; after all, 98 per cent of the population needs what we have to sell!

Market size & potential:
Value-adding

Quantify your total potential. Assess possibilities.

- Who are your potential customers? What are your potential markets?
- Are your markets growing, stable or declining? Why?
- Can you capture any more of the value of any products you currently produce?

Organic marketing choices: To assess your market potential involves an exploration of your total possible sales. Many farmers rely on market-

THE FARMERS' PLEDGE

We pledge that in our farming, processing and marketing we will:

- reject the use of synthetic insecticides, herbicides, fungicides and fertilizers;
- reject the use of GMOs, chemically treated seeds, synthetic toxic materials, irradiation and sewage sludge;
- treat livestock humanely by providing pasture for ruminants, access to outdoors and fresh air for all livestock, banning cruel alterations and using no hormones or antibiotics in feed;
- support agricultural markets and infrastructures that enable small farms to thrive;
- maintain and build healthy soils by farming practices that include rotating crops annually, using compost, cover crops, green manures and reducing tillage;
- conserve natural resources by reducing erosion and pollution of air, soil and water through responsible farming practices;
- maximize the nutritional value of food and feed by practicing careful post harvest handling;
- practice minimal processing for all food products to preserve the natural nutritional value of food: NO use of irradiation, ultra-pasteurization, excessive heat, synthetic preservatives, or GMO processing agents or additives;
- reduce the ecological footprint of farms and homes by limiting energy use and converting to renewable sources of energy;
- reduce food miles by selling produce locally and regionally;
- create beneficial habitat for wildlife and encourage biodiversity;
- help preserve farmland and farming know-how;
- ensure food safety by using potable water for washing crops;
- handle raw manure and soil amendments with care;
- use ethical business practices;
- pay a living wage to all farm workers and acknowledge their freedom of association and their right to collective bargaining;
- treat family members and farm workers with respect and ensure their safety on the farm;
- work in cooperation with other farmers and with the neighboring community to create a more sustainable way of life;
- sustain the land in healthy condition for future generations.

ing diversification—a variety of outlets and incomes to expand their potential revenues. Another method is to add worth to your farm products. Value-adding is one of the most effective ways to increase farm income. Farmers receive an average of about 8 cents of the consumer dollar ($80 billion of an approximately $1 trillion consumer food expenditure according to Stew Smith, professor of sustainable agriculture policy, University of Maine); the rest goes to processors and marketers. Do something different than selling your product like everyone else. Creativity can decrease your vulnerability to elastic production and market conditions and turn small acreage into good profits. There is always room for a new idea. Think about what you are already producing and how you may be able to increase your consumer dollar from it: sheep—wool, clothes, knitted goods; milk—cheese, yogurt; fruits—preserves, etc.

Food producers can savor the fact that almost every person eats every day, several times, and for the most part probably enjoys doing it. However, there is a lot of competition: according to Marketing Intelligence Service's ProducScan figures for consumable items, there were over 11,000 new products introduced in 1996, up from just over 7000 in 1989. Although many of these products will flop (figures are vague, but range from 80 to 94 per cent), there is a lot of jockeying for attention in the marketplace. Your distinct advantage is the quality and integrity of your products. Where and how can you make the most of these attributes and your own skills and level of experience in the marketplace? The table on the next page gives some marketing considerations.

In any venue, there may be constraints to overcome in taking advantage of the full market potential of organic products. Here are a few of them:

- Customer confusion over the meaning of "organic"—the difficulty of differentiating between sustainable organic and industrial organic foods and of understanding how these relate to other marketing terms such as "natural," "grass fed," "free range," "humanely raised," "locally grown"
- Immature markets—the organic market is still young. You will have to do some basic marketing research in your area to determine your most viable options and outlets
- Distance from large urban centers, limited local markets
- Lack of processing & distribution infrastructure
- Regulation and certification procedures

SOME MARKETING CONSIDERATIONS

Venue	Marketing	Cost/Benefit Analysis Considerations	Issues
Community Supported Farms (CSA): Member fee in exchange for a "season" of produce or products	Very interactive; Membership limits make for very focused marketing & promotion.	Win/Win: assured sales; Community development; Interdependence; Farmer/consumer equitability; Diversity. Possibile farm-to-farm cooperation to enhance offerings, strengthen community. Must be organized, responsible to manage commitments to membership.	Must have confidence and experience in production; This is not best start-up option, you must grow into it!
Farmers' Markets	Interactive; Develop customer base through display, quality, education, consistency, diversity plus good signage!	Direct market means best price for product. Community involvement. Proximity to established grower markets is helpful. No assurance of sales: product quality and marketing imperative.	Can be exhausting: loading; hauling; set-up; selling. Selling "you," farm must be well represented: charisma and enthusiasm good for sales!
Farmstands	Interactive to hands off. Display, consistency, signage & promotion.	Direct marketing, best price for product. Owning, managing infrastructure gives self-determination but also more responsibility, cost.	Location and diversity of offerings important marketing considerations.
Institutions:Schools, Day Care, Elder Care	Single-contact sales.Important to manage relationship, issues.	Price subject to institution—scale, type, funding.Programs throughout the country working on ways to increase farm-institution interactions	Consistency and quality important. Immature market, do your footwork.
Local Stores	Single-contact sales.Focus on local, fresh, high-quality	Wholesale prices. Uncertain demand and turnover can lead to quality control issues. Must be ready to deal with quantity, packing and certifications required, ASK!	Hard to receive best prices in conventional markets, check co-ops and health food stores.
Mail-Order	Internet or promotional development key. Follow-through a must.	Premium price. Takes time and some overhead to develop. Issues: individual order processing, packaging, timeliness and updating of materials.	Research shipping methods, consider quality, insurance, minimums and return policy.
Pick-Your-Own Operations	Community promotion; signage, instruction.	Equitable prices with low labor input. Supports low-income community and food supply connection.	Consider safety of area and insurance issues.
Producers Co-op	Cooperative sales for less individual marketing	Infrastructure and management important. Effective distribution requires scale that supports costs.	Uniformity: packing and quality standards
Restaurant: Direct Sales	Single-contact sales; work closely with chef	Premium prices for highest quality, clean! Must develop relationship by communication, consistency.	Chefs are BUSY. Must take initiative to develop account.
Restaurant: CSA	Single-contact sales	Premium prices—Demands responsibility, quality, presentation.	Plan with chef, be reliable

SECTION 4: MARKETING STRATEGIES

The goal of this section is to help determine your most effective product and promotional strategies.

Example: Recognizing that the Ithaca Farmers Market was already rich with quality vegetables, Laurie Todd identified a niche of her own: melons. Although she continued to sell a variety of fruits and vegetables, Laurie grew a loyal customer base at the market by offering an amazing selection of top quality melons not available anywhere else. Even on the slowest days, 'The Melon Lady' rarely took any home.

Product strategies:
Diversity & production potential

Determine the most beneficial balance between market potential of products offered and production issues. Think about diversity and effort-reward allocations.

- What is the scope of your product offerings?
- What are your real limits to growth?
- What is the cost-benefit of producing a greater diversity or specializing?

Diversification and specialization: Diversification is the key to stability. Diverse offerings catch the eye and encourage sales. However, your scope must take into account your ability to do things well and not overextend your resources. Sometimes extra products are a drain on valuable resources: time, personnel, space, etc. Consider diversity in all areas: products, markets, clientele and labor. Specialization can also offer you a real advantage in some markets. The "Melon Lady" just mentioned is one example.

Production potential: Think about your resources: land, equipment, personnel, capital, experience—consider value-adding possibilities. Production potential in a diverse system is a case of balancing cost and benefit, a give and take of possibilities. Look at the big picture; consider your quality of life objectives and what is enough. Write these things down. Develop a sensible plan that balances concerns, potentials, needs and possibilities.

On and off farm: Many of the farmers that I have spoken to were looking for a way to work on-site, happy to give up the 'outside job' when their farm income could support it. Joel Salatin and his family have created a number of on-farm ventures to suit their creative and productive interests. Family members are given the freedom to initiate and manage income ventures that interest them. As a result, the farm thrives economically from the diversity of revenues and family members gain the skill and confidence to manage their own projects.

Many others had compelling reasons to keep their off-farm income or return to it at some point in their lives. This question of income diversity is another one to consider when determining the question of production: does it make sense for your family to retain or develop an outside income? Barbara Smith of Meadowsweet Farm in Lodi, N.Y. has found outside employment to be worthwhile for her family. Her other job—indexing books— can be done at home, providing both flexibility and income stability to the household income. Another advantage: she enjoys it! Other jobs can also provide the security of health and retirement benefits to those who desire these services.

Price & quality issues

Develop a written explanation of your pricing policy to guide pricing decisions and share with your patrons:

- What is the going market rate for products similar to yours?
- What is the break-even price of your products?
- How will you communicate your pricing to your customers?
- What are the qualities they will be willing to pay for?

Courage to charge a good price: There are two key issues in pricing: what people will pay for a product and what you need to charge to afford to produce it. Don't be afraid to charge a good price for high quality products. As Joel Salatin asserts, "You get what you pay for, and that includes food." This may seem like a difficult truth to sell in a nation that has come to expect the low market prices of a subsidized food system. And when small-scale organic growers compete with corporate "cheap foods" in the marketplace, the result is not always pretty for the little guy. But, believe it or not, the result of the "cheap" food mentality—the undermining of quality for profit—is creating a marketplace of high opportunity for sustainable growers and producers. Just because we can't compete in certain arenas does not mean that we can't be successful in the marketplace. After all, we don't need every food dollar spent; we just need to manage our marketing equations to ensure that we know what is enough and how to earn that.

As events reveal the real subsidies and costs—in ever more blatant deterioration of human and animal health and the stability of natural systems—we can succeed by offering healing interconnection and quality alternatives, without the corporate-scale price wars. Recognizing that scandals may well continue to rock industrial economics, we are likely to see a growing response to market choices that offer ethical safe haven and community. The other side of the equation is proactive, up to us: providing necessary goods and services and straightforwardly communicating the sustainable marketing principles through which we supply them.

Determining product pricing

Price = Breakeven Point + Reasonable Profit is a very general equation for determining product pricing. The market may or may not support this price. It is important to monitor market prices for goods of similar type and quality to keep current on what customers are paying for like products.

No matter what price you need to charge, in the end, a product is only worth what someone is willing to pay for it. And it is only worth producing if its earnings are worth your time. Two mechanisms for increasing the market's price ceiling are to educate the public about the real value of your product and to increase the real quality. Generally speaking, it is better to give away product than drop the price way down. Whereas people become concerned about the quality of arbitrarily low-priced goods, everyone loves to get something free! One idea is to use something you have a lot of as free incentive to encourage customers to purchase more of other products.

When selling an item—such as handwork—that may feel expensive when all of the related services are quoted as one lump sum, itemize related costs separately. This invites your customers into the production process and teaches them the true cost, in your time and efforts. A wool skein, for example, involves washing, picking and carding, etc. and justifies overheads that are still unfamiliar to many who have been weaned on everyday low prices. Some further guides to pricing:

If you raise prices, tell people why.
Generally speaking, never lower your prices
Use volume pricing—people are used to the idea of getting more for a bargain.
Price relative to market; make sure your product matches your price.
Tout your quality—higher prices encourage customer loyalty if you educate about quality.
Don't apologize for pricing—explain why the prices are high.
Add income cushions for "unforeseen" disasters into your pricing equations.
Don't give rebates. They will move product in the short term but tend not to pay in the long run.

Creating a sustainable customer base requires charging a fair price:

one that is fair to you and to your patrons. Again, do not undercharge. Instead, have a ready explanation of your pricing policy. People need to be educated about real costs. Be confident about disclosing your pricing methods. Providing pricing information up front will alleviate the sense of uncertainty when it comes time to pay. While most people will pay more for quality, they also hate to feel gouged. Hammurabi's Code (18th Century B.C.) judged such offenses very seriously: "If a man has committed highway robbery and has been caught, that man shall be put to death."

Research market prices

The Rodale Institute has developed an effective tool to help you determine a competitive price for your products. They call it the Organic Price Index™ (OPX™). The index allows you to compare organic and conventional prices in markets across the country. Launched with East and West coast market indicators, The New Farm® is now in the process of expanding to include more regional sites. It is regularly updated and available for reference online at www.newfarm.org/opx.

Calculate your break-even price

In order to determine the break-even price for your products in the marketplace, you must establish mechanisms for quantifying "enough" recompense for crop value and your time. Many people begin by answering the question "What am I willing to work for?" and set an hourly minimum. Joel Salatin chose the figure $20-$25/hour in 1998. At Pleasant Valley Farm in Argyle, N.Y., Paul and Sandy Arnold currently value their time at $30/hour. They have also established a $10,000 per acre rule: all crops that they market must achieve these standard returns. If they do not, the Arnolds either innovate a different way to sell or manage the crop in order to achieve this performance level; continue to grow it for diversity reasons (changing expectation from profit to other standards); or stop growing it commercially altogether. The key to any valuation is a good record keeping system that tracks the resource exchange for money: inputs, time, market interactions and space utilized.

Here is how the Arnolds worked out the profitability of land used to grow sugar snap peas:

Records kept: Amount sold, price, field space planted
    538 pints @ $3/pint = $1814
    Field space: 2700 square feet
        Converted to acres: 2700/43,560 = .062 acre
           Income per acre: $1814/.062 = $26,032
Result: Passed the $10,000/acre rule.

And here is how they tested out the $30/hour rule for beans:

Records kept: total time to harvest, wash and prepare crop for sale or market

    Avg. picker picks 25 pounds/hour (includes crating)

        Price of beans: $2.50/lb.

           Per hour income: 25 x 2.50 = $62.50

Result: Passed the $30/hour rule.

In short, here is a review of what you need to know or decide to make good pricing decisions:

1. Time spent on task (keep good records)
2. What you are willing to work for per hour—don't sell yourself short; don't commit highway robbery
3. Overheads and fixed costs
4. Price and quality of comparable goods in the venue where you are selling.

Promotional strategies

Outline your best promotional strategies including how, when and where to connect with your customers.

- Where and how will you promote your products?
- What aspects of your products or business are important to your patrons?
- How can you sell yourself?

Let them eat image? Organic marketing must reject the hyper-corporate model by filling needs rather than arbitrarily promoting consumption for profit. Vital interests—like our health, the exploited workforce, global stability—are harmed by the hidden costs of producing extraneous, inferior products no matter how cheap. Skillful hype tries to hide that. Promotion too must be held responsible.

Advertising and the fattening of the corporation

In the passion for corporate revenues, conventional advertising—the "growth hormone" of marketing—fosters consumer desire and discontent. Most of us face these assault, but we all bear the costs: the average schoolchild will be exposed to over 50,000 TV commercials per year. You can shut off your television, but escaping advertising is much more difficult. Advertising has more surreptitious channels, as we will explore below. The food industry in particular, led by multinational corporate interests, is one of the most deceptive and dishonest industries to have plagued human history.

In her meticulously documented book *Food Politics—How the Food Industry Influences Nutrition and Health,* Marion Nestle describes a legacy of governmental endorsement of industry products and concerns. Well-meaning nutritionists and scientists are forced—by intimidation, upper echelon pressure and the risk of losing livelihoods—to mince their words and significantly alter their public health messages in order to appease the industry. These "sanctioned advertisements," Nestle believes, are implicated in the current general confusion and ignorance about diet.

Take the deconstruction of whole foods into the mystique of their parts. This popular method for hijacking nutritional concerns, in which a whole-food diet is forsaken for the mystification of the Recommended Daily Allowance, now sells us protein, calcium and zinc…hard to find in farm stands and the non-packaged aisles! The isolated properties of nutrients are used to sell food products with slogans like: "strong bones and healthy teeth," "the breakfast of champions," and the ubiquitous "provides (enter a number) essential vitamins and minerals."

Corporate "educational" and "public service" information pours into under-funded schools, health care facilities, news media and community organizations desperate for relevant scientific literature. The mythology is that initiatives like these are providing a public health service. But let's take a closer look at just one example. According to nutritional specialist Dr. Joel Fuhrman, one of the leading questions he is asked is "How can I be sure I am getting enough protein?" With a quick review of the protein in a variety of diets, Fuhrman demonstrates that it is, in fact, difficult *not* to get enough protein in any diet that provides you enough calories to survive. The concern has no basis in fact.

The Lancet and other medical publications—including T. Colin Campbell's China Project, which has been recognized as the most comprehensive study yet on the multiple causes of disease—have been representing a very different concern for years. Nutritional studies have long shown a much lower need for protein than "educational" advertising would lead us to believe. Even more disturbing is that excess protein intake has been strongly implicated in systemic loss of calcium—the highest levels of osteoporosis are found in countries whose national diets contain the highest levels of protein. Campbell puts it this way: "The body needs only about 8-10 per cent of its calories as protein. Anything more than that, particularly if it is animal protein, is associated with a wide variety of chronic degenerative diseases." In this light current low-carbohydrate diets, with their implicit reliance on protein, look even more disturbing.

There are many issues involved in the effects of what we put into our bodies. The concern is that, by infiltrating the institutions entrusted with educating us and selling us on promises like "strong bones and teeth," the food industry—and promotional advertisement—has crossed an ethical line. Public health is undercut by the over-consumption that the same advertising instigates. So what is the consequece of this type of misleading marketing? A kind of nutritional Babylon that leaves the public no clarity for making healthful dietary and food-purchasing choices. Advertising can be more dangerous than we ever give it credit for.

A world of difference in promotional marketing

Visitors to Sweden or Japan might be amazed to see honest advertising. Japan has won accolades from travelers since the first century AD for the honesty of their business practices. Japanese businesses, in examples noted recently, post true prices (including tax and fees), do not put down their competitors and do not use comparisons to insinuate that their products are better than those their competitors offer. Sweden has enforced laws against deceptive advertising since the 1970s. The measures appear to be effective; while US opinion polls consistently rank advertisers just above car salesmen for respectability, Swedes defend the integrity of their advertising.

Although the U.S. does have laws against deceptive advertising (see "The Legal Guide for Starting and Running a Small Business" by Fred Steingold online at www.Nolo.com), they haven't controlled small print limitations, exaggeration, unscrupulous follow through and understatement (or lack of indication) of risk. Studies show our populace growing increasingly distrustful of advertising.

Given the human cost of this hype and distraction, you might question the ethics of adding your own company's voice to the cacophony assailing the public domain. It happens that more than two-thirds of established small businesses in the US operate profitably without advertising (NOLO, 2001). They may list their businesses and take advantage of many other opportunities for promotion, but they do not rely on conventional paid advertising. While large companies are spending almost $650 for every person in the US each year to bombard the average individual with over 2,500 ads per day, there appears to be a more sustainable and peaceful way to market: pinpoint where your customer base will be looking for the information and advertise there instead of blanketing the whole community.

In surveys, over half of patrons say they made their initial choice of a product or service on the recommendation of other customers or professionals in the field. Our communal nature is to share the things that we value with others. Hard to believe in the roar of commercials…but successful marketing has little need of an advertising budget. What it demands instead is a plan that enables a slow, steady business growth that develops and maintains a satisfied customer base. It is primarily your personal contacts (and those of your patrons)—not advertising—that will make your business grow and will sustain it. What seems to count is not what your business says about itself, but what others say about it.

Where to promote

Listings. Yellow pages, farm directory listings, Internet farm locators (www.NewFarm.com, www.LocalHarvest.com), "notification" ads: penny saver, community papers, organization newsletters, classified ads.

Handouts. Use any opportunity to educate your customers about your business and products, food quality issues, nutritional data, recipes, trivia relating to unfamiliar or popular items: fliers, brochures, newsletters and recipes can be hand written or laid out on the computer. All can be easily duplicated by inexpensive speed printing at your local print shop.

Signage & display. Colorful and informative signs and abundant diverse displays will help to grab customer attention and draw them to your establishment. According to a University of Tennessee survey of roadside market shoppers, 74 per cent learn of a stand's location by following signs (24 per cent found stands by word of mouth and 2 per cent responded to media ads). Make your signs visible. Driving at 50 mph, a motorist has only three seconds to assess a roadside business. Place primary signs 1/2-mile from the business in both directions, clearly directing passersby to your location: "Homegrown Tomatoes, 1/2 mile on Right."

A clean, rural "down on the farm" image appeals to customers. Simple, creative signs that are easy to see and understand are important: dark on light backgrounds; fruit or vegetable cutouts; basic, large letters (about 1/5 as wide as they are high). Customers are often afraid to ask, so clearly identify and price each product display.

Keep your displays neat. Create eye appeal by contrasting colors; spread out the "big draw" items like corn, melons, apples and tomatoes and place "impulse buys" like baked goods, maple syrup and popcorn in high visibility positions—impulsive purchases often account for more than half of total sales.

Word of mouth. Word of mouth advertising is not a passive means of achieving customer support, it is an active business policy of encouraging the positive and discouraging the negative. Statistically, customers complain to an average of 11 other people when they feel they have received poor service. Far fewer people volunteer about receiving outstanding service—although they

The buzz about your business will ultimately determine its success.

will give valuable recommendations when asked. Obviously it's important to minimize any opportunities for customer dissatisfaction. To favorably impress your customers, offer outstanding products and service, do something differently and better, appeal to their good sense and ideology.

Internet. Seventy-seven per cent of the public are using the Internet to gather information. This is a terrific customer service tool that invites educational material, sales offerings and details such as directions to your farm.

Informational websites are an opportunity for anyone interested in your type of products to find you. E-mail is a direct way to educate your customers and inform them of offerings. Farm websites are as unique as farms themselves. Check out as many as possible to get a feel for the myriad ways to use this tool. Free help is available at www.visionweb.com and www.newfarm.org (click on marketing).

There are also shared websites that provide small businesses free listings—this is a great way to let people know you are out there. Two popular ones are www.localharvest.org and www.newfarm.org/farmlocator/index.php.

According to a study done in 1997 by Sun Microsystems into how people read on the Web, the simple conclusion was "they don't." Every page is competing with millions more for attention. Among their suggestions: highlight key words; use bullet lists, frequent subheadings, paragraphs containing exactly *one* idea; and offer nothing too difficult to maneuver.

Events. If you are opening a storefront, stand or U-pick establishment, a grand opening is a great way to make people aware of your new venture. You may want to wait a couple of weeks after the start to be sure things are running smoothly.

Make your event a news item, twice! Promote it in a press release and the local calendar and then write and submit a description of the event with pictures.

Give the kids something to do. Parents will be relieved and kids will want to come back.

Make invitations, get commitments—Be sure to send invitations or make calls to friends and family, acquaintances, the mailman, your dentist etc.to ensure attendance at festivities. Get commitments. If a photographer is coming, you want foot traffic or activity to create a good photo opportunity. Don't be shy about calling on your friends for assistance—they are sure to have fun in the process.

Press release—If you are having an event at your farm or elsewhere, draft a press release for local papers. It's free advertising and newspapers are always looking for news. Submit the press release to the reporter who covers local news and follow-up with a phone call to see if the reporter can make the event. Press releases are also a great way to introduce a new business, let the community know that you are doing something new, or welcome in a new season or crop.

Articles and letters to the editor. These are both terrific ways to educate your community and make them aware of opportunities to support your farm. Write often, talk to your local paper about submitting local interest stories, keep your eyes open for relevant issues to comment on, introduce concerns and provide alternatives.

Calandar. Be sure to submit events, picking schedules and openings to local calendars in weekly papers, on-line listings, or free guides to community happenings.

Photos. When you let the paper know about an event, new crop you're growing or any other business milestone, ask if they can send a photographer. If they cannot, take your own photos and submit them to the editor of the paper after the fact along with a short description for community interest.

What to promote

Your story. Use pictures when you can. Let your customers get to know you. Who are you? What are you doing and why?

Introductions to the farm, family, farmers, products, what might set you apart and make people want to support your business.

Yourself! Appearance and attitude matter.

Your contact information. Make sure to include this on every piece of information that you distribute. Business cards are an inexpensive way to solidify contacts and encourage sales.

Your positive image. Some important elements of it are: organized, reliable, clean, uncluttered, good smelling (no kidding! This is important to customer sales.) Learn to run a high quality business—if your products and services are not good enough to talk about, they will not be recommended. Presenting an ordered image begins with actually getting it together. Put in the time to do this first and the image will be built on substance.

Your significant (and real) point of difference. Significant means it is important to people, real means it does actually exist. An example is M&M's assertion that their candies "melt in your mouth, not in your hands." Personality is relevant here: in the organic market, idiosyncrasy can sell by emphasizing character and confidence.

Honest product and price information. One study claimed that it takes about seven times as much effort to win back disgruntled customers as it did to get them to begin with. Customers take your promises seriously.

Your goals. If you have a farm stand or pickup site, post anything that will enlist your customer's support for your goals and direction. Tell them what you are all about: organic certification, Farmers' Pledge, mission statement.

Your products. Products should be clean, attractive and ready to use when possible. Explain your products—how to use them, store them, how they will benefit customers. Sample, sample, sample! Let quality speak for itself. Everyone appreciates being able to try before buying.

Your good reputation. Develop one; vigilantly guard it by maintaining the quality of your products, services and promotional materials. The continuity of your company is an important factor in your market success, developing an image that works and sticking to it develops trust and long-term commitment by giving your customers and staff something to hold onto.

Packaging & labeling

Attractive packaging can make an average product something special. Make it distinctive, but keep the packaging down—use as little as possible without hindering the objective. Convenience is expected, but customers are thrifty; they do not want to buy more than they can comfortably use.

If you are planning to direct market your products, you may want to consider bulk displays and units (a dozen ears of corn, a quart of beans), or per-item pricing. Packing and selling by weight involves the use of state inspected sealed scales that conform to weights and measures standards. If you do pack by weight, avoid fines by ensuring that products are appropriately labeled and at or above the stated weight.

If you are selling to an intermediary, ask for the specific pack standard for your products. Some venues will expect things to be packed a certain way, and in a competitive market, you may only get one chance to get it right. The US Food and Drug Administration determines and enforces labeling regulations for what can and cannot be legally claimed on labels and advertisements. The National Organic Program standards require very specific labeling for "organic" products. Be sure to check for specifics regarding any packaged foods, including dairy and meat at www.attra.ncat.org.

Placement and selling strategies

List ways to increase the market potential of your products through people, placement and presentation.

- What placement, people, organizations could help increase your sales potential?
- How could you engage customer action to increase the "stickiness" of your product's image?
- How can you present your products to reflect highest quality and value?

Tipping theory

Chaos theory describes the instability of dynamic systems: at any point a small push can have large consequences. Similarly, social movements and epidemics—such as disease transmission, crime waves, the emergence of fashion trends, the phenomenon of "word of mouth," rise of best-sellers—have been shown to move in the same way. The point where that "small push" cascades slow momentum into raging epidemic has been dubbed the Tipping Point.

Marketing is the process of engaging transformation. In trying to "tip" an idea, attitude or product we are trying to change our audience in some small critical respect. Tipping points are convenient, if rare, shortcuts, ways to make a lot out of a little. Inviting that phenomenon while holding the values of the organic approach requires some care. Still, understanding this phenomenon is instructive in influencing our market in small ways; a powerful testament to the importance of peer and community influence on marketing success (Gladwell, 2000):

Law of the Few. Purchasing habits have much more to do with image than we might think—what people buy often has little to do with the product, but everything to do with its users, or perceived users. People in your community who are connectors, mavens and salesmen are responsible for starting word of mouth epidemics. Can you identify any people like this? Engage them in your message and they will do your work for you.

Stickiness factor. Changing the content of communication to make a message so memorable it sticks in someone's mind and compels them to action. Promotions showing maps and giving customers something to *do*—like clipping and bringing in a coupon—tend to be stickier.

Power of context. Epidemics are sensitive to the conditions of the times and places in which they occur. It is the small indications of quality and attention that make big changes in market success. A fascinating example of this concept is how the New York City subway system became a safer place when supervised by an individual who believed in the broken window theory: that crimes large and small are more likely to occur in areas that look like they are uncared for. By managing the image of the subway—persistently removing graffiti from the cars, cutting down on fare jumpers and keeping things in good working order—the incidence of serious crime decreased significantly. To a large degree, people act on their impressions. According to a 1994 Ohio State University study, "Consumer Opinions of Roadside and Farmer's Markets," 88 per cent of people prefer to buy produce directly from the farm and 90 per cent believe that they can get better quality produce by doing so. The study goes on to suggest making your establishment "farm-like"—giving it a down-home feel evokes people's confidence.

"Coopetition"

Coopetition refers to cooperative competition. It involves identifying another business that markets to the same target market as you—but is not in direct competition with your products—and working together for mutual benefit. An incredibly lucrative example of this is the relationship between Starbucks and Atlantic Records. Some 22 million people pass through Starbucks each week, and so far they have purchased approximately 350,000 Artist's Choice picks with their coffee. This is successful coopetition.

An agricultural example of coopetition in action is producer-only markets, in which farmers are allowed to sell only what they grow; all vendors benefit from the increased draw of a larger marketplace.

SECTION 5: PRODUCT AND SERVICE DESCRIPTIONS

The goal is to identify precisely where you want your business to be, to create a mission statement.

- What business are you in?
- What do you sell, to whom, & how?
- What is unique about your business?
- What are the needs that your business is addressing?

Planning your destination

Where do you *want* to be? This step involves pulling all of your insights from the previous sections together to make a decision about what your business is actually marketing and how it will do that. Implicit in this process are:

1. Creating realistic goals
2. Clarifying your vision and making sure that your family/partners agree
3. Putting your goals in writing by creating a mission statement.

Begin by answering all of the questions posed in Sections 1-4. Review your answers and those of your business partners with the goal of coming to a workable marketing image that you can agree upon. Once you have envisioned together what you want your business to be, *put it in writing*. This process will save you from your own enthusiasm! It guards against scattered and fragmented efforts and expensive distractions.

Like all aspects of marketing, your mission statement is not meant to be a static document. It is a working guide that should be revisited and assessed as your business grows so that it continues to reflect your changing needs, experience, interests and goals. Start small and add on as you work out the details of your marketing plan. However, it is important to take the time to create one when you are starting out, or wherever you are in your farm business venture. A marketing mission statement:

1. Focuses the goals and desires of your business with helpful specifics—this is a road map for your progress and a quick reference to determine if a new direction fits in with your goals.
2. Gets everyone who's involved in the project on the same page and creates a foundation for approaching daily tasks.
3. Provides a succinct means of letting others know what you are doing—do they want to support that goal?

Here is an example of a mission statement from Early Morning Organic Farm in Genoa, N.Y. Laurie Pattington and Anton Burkett include their statement on the back of their price list and order form handout:

Early Morning's Mission Statement

Early Morning Organic Farm strives to balance the short term and long term social, economic and ecological needs of ourselves and our local community.

We endeavor:

to preserve the integrity of our natural environment with farming practices which minimize soil erosion and chemical pollution of the air, water and soil.

to actively maintain and increase biodiversity, soil vitality and ecosystem stability.

to produce nutritious food for our local community, creating lasting and meaningful, person-to-person relationships with our customers, which reconnect individuals to their food source.

to complete an integrated nutrient and fertility cycle within the farm in order to minimize our use of external inputs such as fossil fuels, other petroleum products and off farm manure.

to maximize our food production per acre while efficiently managing our available resources in order to compensate for development pressure on the land from suburban sprawl and the consolidation of agricultural resources by large conventional agribusiness.

to raise livestock with compassion in a system which mimics their natural habitat and facilitates and utilizes their natural habits.

to grow organic vegetables without the use of pesticides, fungicides, herbicides, or synthetic fertilizers.

to provide the farm and farmers with a modest income with which to raise our family and further our social and ecological goals.

to create beauty on this land and in the relationships between workers, livestock, crops, our natural environment and our local community.

to further the trade of farming by offering internships to aspiring farmers.

Mission statement as a marketing tool. Post your mission statement or print it in your brochure or other handouts. Although many people will not read it in its entirety, other interested people will. It is an outline of what you stand for that customers can use to assess how much they want to support your endeavors through the purchase of your products. Be sure to keep it current with your goals and then make it as visible as possible.

Your mission statement will not only tell the values and goals of your business; its existence hints at other qualities important to consumers: integrity, stability, thoughtfulness, ability to follow through, organization and direction. It draws them into your consciencious world, lets them feel a part of your bigger picture and invites them to support it through the purchase of your products.

Your turn! Once you have determined what you would like to do in your business, be sure to learn what it takes to manage the project and develop (or seek out) the skills to do it. Seek wise counsel. Identify people who are where you want to be and find out how they got there.

SECTION 6: MANAGEMENT AND ASSESSMENT

The goal is assessment and management of your marketing plan.

- Is your marketing plan successful?
- How can you best manage your market interactions?
- What records do you need to keep and how will you keep them?

Initiating market contacts

Everyone is busy these days, so when initiating contacts, remember that you are the one who will benefit from making a deal here:

Be proactive, don't be put off if someone doesn't call you (or call you back)—*you call them.*

Be prepared.

Find out whom you need to talk to. Know their name, responsibilities, contact info, best time to call or approach them—don't start out on a wrong foot by coming at an inconvenient time.

If possible, make an appointment.

If you have an appointment, come a few minutes early, but not too far ahead of time

Appearance matters—be neat, professional.

Be informed about your own business and how you can help their business.

Bring handouts and product information. Print your farm name, address and contact information on every page of your material.

Bring samples—top quality—and present them attractively.

Follow up by telephone in a timely manner. Make sure you are talking to the right person to make the decision that you need.

Follow-up by letter or e-mail. Be specific—clarify what you discussed and any decisions that you made.

Always deliver what you promise.

Making the sale

Sales are the mature fruits of a marketing relationship. People have needs, and they want to have them met. The art of persuasion involves first determining how your product will meet the needs of your market contact—then how to convey that. This is equally applicable in approaching a head chef with a product, creating a CSA core or introducing your customers to new foods.

Depending on where you are marketing and to whom (middleperson or final consumer) the needs your product will fill differ greatly. First know your own products, know their attributes and limitations inside and out, brainstorm selling points. Then learn about the needs of each constituent in your marketing scenario and line up the benefits and needs. The more clearly you are able to draw this picture, the more irresistible your products will be.

Our influencing techniques are designed largely for gaining agreement and reward from people who are much like ourselves. Aware of what drives our own decisions, we are attuned to those who share similar motivations, values and ways of thinking about the world. You have a natural audience with people you understand. It is fruitful to consider where and with whom you have this natural connectivity in your market planning. If you want to be truly effective in influencing the decisions of people—and markets—that are different from you, you must first learn something about their motivations, values and ways of thinking about things. Then you must learn and apply techniques applicable to their situation. You must do your homework.

Behaviorist Allen Harrison says in order to enhance your influence in relationships, be sure to respect and augment the other person's sense of importance, sense of competence and sense of being likeable.

Managing your market

Sustainable marketing =
quality interactions + quality, life-friendly products

If you are not personally selling your products, someone is selling them…or not. A key to making sales is managing the channels of distribution. Make sure that everyone from the packers to the clerks knows how to handle your products. The best bet is to keep it simple and easy to understand. Do whatever possible to help your middlepersons—clerks, chefs, etc.—sell your products. Cultivate relationships—be kind to all staff that you deal with. Bring samples; the more they know and like you (and your goods), the more they will be salespeople for your products.

Reputation is everything in business. If our marketing activities support those people we work with, we will reap the rewards personally and financially. If our activities are harmful, aggressive or deceitful, at some point people will begin to treat us warily—becoming apprehensive and suspicious on account of our bad reputation. Be wary of attaching your name to anything that you don't fully support ideologically. People are watching you; they want to support your good efforts.

Recordkeeping

Those who cannot remember the past are condemned to repeat it.

—George Santayana

Marketing consultant Robert McMath discusses a phenomenon that he calls corporate Alzheimers. He's studied the mechanisms that lead to the loss of a historical perspective and the resulting repetition of past trials and errors. It turns out this is an extremely important issue in farm businesses, especially multigenerational ones. It is ridiculously easy to lose history. Transparency and communication are essential; taking the time to let your crew know how and why you are making marketing decisions will give them the perspective necessary to make their own decisions if and when they are in the position to do so. Understanding the underlying issues also gives your employees a tool for expressing the directives that motivate your business; there will be less of the head shaking, grumbling and eye rolling that can undermine the "because I said so" approach.

Keeping good records of your decisions, including notes explaining changes along the way, assures that what is so clear in your head does not get lost in time and the shuffle of employees who pass through your business. This will increase your efficiency and connectedness while encouraging participation. Inviting others into the process will take the pressure of being indispensable off your shoulders and expand the creative potential available to guide your marketing decisions. This key to long-term success is familiar to farmers: prepare the ground.

Again, KEEP GOOD RECORDS. Records are needed for efficient planning, performance assessment, decision-making and financial reporting. In marketing a product you must establish a value for the time, labor, inputs, space and expenditures that they represent. This enables you to assign realistic prices and track time for value information. If you are certified organic, planning to certify, or looking for documentation assistance, you may find ATTRA's free forms (800 346-9140) helpful (ATTRA stands for Appropriate Technology Transfer for Rural Areas). They are designed to record practices, inputs and activities that demonstrate compliance with the National Organic Standards, but provide a good template for easy recording in the following categories: Field Crops; Livestock; Orchard, Vineyard, & Berry Crops; and Organic Market Farming Forms.

You do not need a computer or spreadsheet for effective record keeping. Choose a method that you will be able to easily follow and stick with it for everything you've got. If you have had the experience of trying to recreate a year's activity at tax time, you know what an inefficient, sloppy misery it can be. You cannot base sound marketing decisions on imaginary numbers.

Assessing post-purchase satisfaction

Sometimes in the feedback process your market will define itself in unexpected ways. If it does so, let it! Educate yourself and figure out how to capitalize on it.

When we began our business—making raw manna breads and snacks for what we perceived to be a small and specific customer base—we were amazed by the response of a group that we hadn't expected: the growing community of people requiring gluten-free foods. When we realized the connection, we quickly changed some of our marketing materials to speak to this group of people. This has become one of our most fruitful selling points. Often there are needs out there that we may not have recognized—when these opportunities fall in our laps, we should be flexible. Watch who is buying your products, get out and talk to people, let them tell you what they like and expand your promotional and market scope when you recognize possibilities.

Likewise, keep your eyes open for issues. Bad news is as welcome as good news here because it will help you to refine your focus in the direction of success. Be honest in looking at what is working and what is not. Beware of excuses. It is no failure to learn and revise as you go; the failure is in continuing to follow a path that is not working for you.

Reviewing your marketing plan

Take your time, try different things, make market contacts and get a feel for how marketing works before you commit to something big. Plan for all the seasons of the year and of life; prepare for change. Heraclitus (500 B.C.) reminds us that: "in the circumference of a circle, the beginning and end are common." This is also true for marketing:

Work through the planning process
Take action
Observe, measure and record results
Compare actual vs. planned results
Explain differences
Initiate changes
REPEAT

Here are some questions to help you assess the effectiveness of your marketing plan:

Is it productive? Review the yield or net income per unit of resource.

Is it stable? Consider the degree to which market productivity is constant in the face of small disturbances.

Is it sustainable? Reflect on your system's ability to maintain productivity in the eventuality of a major disturbance such as that caused by the failure of a crop or major piece of equipment. What are your points of vulnerability and how can you extend your foundations?

Is it equitable? Analyze the distributive aspects of your plan—the more equitable the system, the more evenly resources are shared. Have you made an accurate assessment of "enough"?

Quick review

Sustainable marketing hinges on interconnection, quality, principle and responsibility—not just on products. Production is the *result* of the other considerations, not their engineer. Sustainable marketing is needs-driven. It both quantifies and qualifies itself by defining limits to growth and parameters of value. It is firmly rooted in context: holistic, embracing. Traditional—exploitive—marketing, on the other hand, defines itself by what it wants to sell you; its marketing approach sets itself no limits, lacks a foundational responsibility for the integrity of our common resources and defers to the wisdom of the market (rather than natural laws) in the consideration of consequences. The addition of one value—sustainability—to the equation demands that you bring these issues with you to market.

One word of warning: there is a time and energy lag between recognizing opportunity and engaging it. To learn sustainable marketing requires patience and practice, trial and understanding. To be successful and sustainable, you must be willing to adjust to nature's pace. If you're fresh from the races (so to speak), it might seem a bit slow at first.

Chapter 4
Final keys to marketing success

The real key to successful marketing lies in taking yourself, not just your products, to market. Organic marketing is relationship marketing. Your best marketing strategy is to create the best business that you can: treat people well, sell high quality products, stick to your principles, be generous and make customer service the cornerstone of your interactions.

My favorite marketing guidance comes from Billie Best, a marketing professional and aspiring farmer who claims that the rules of marketing are the same whether you are selling cars or organic carrots:

Know your market audience:
Who are they? Where are they? How do they live? What do they care about?

Have a clear message:
What are you selling? What are the benefits of buying it?

Maintain visibility:
Get your message to your market in as many ways as possible, as often as possible.

Be consistent:
Repeat the same message. Appear in the same place over and over again.

Be a good communicator:
Stay in touch with your market. Be responsive to inquiries.

Love your customers:
Listen well. Be generous. Anticipate market demand.

Since marketing is a powerful and persuasive force, future-minded folks use the tool with responsibility and discretion. There are many reasons why people buy products with few real benefits or even harmfulness to health or common welfare. In *The Botany of Desire*, Michael Pollan argues that the universal human desire for sweetness—along with the desires for beauty, intoxication and control—has proven to be a force, not just in the marketplace, but in evolution. He argues that this desire has been noticed and exploited by the reproductive habits of certain plants. Strange to consider, but it begs the question: who is in control of human—and market—momentum? Humans? The market itself, in its offer of endless sweetness?

No matter what you think of his theory, it is worthwhile to consider who is at the steering wheel, who or what controls our susceptibility to the market's enticements. If we manage to rediscover lost sources of sweetness—in nature, beauty, connectedness—if we acknowledge the toll and take back the initiative, then on some level the market will let go of us, replaced by vitalizing relationships predicated on compassion and self-discipline.

Most of us know how to make seeds grow: lay them down in fertile soil...water them as necessary...give them attention but don't overwhelm them...shine the sun of opportunity on them...give them some time and space to mature. The same goes for your Marketing Plan. Enjoy the process.

In the end, what it comes down to is how much people can really be made to care about themselves.
—Joan Dye Gussow 1991

RESOURCES

Marketing and business assistance and training

Local Chamber of Commerce—clearinghouse for small business programs and information sources—do not have to be a member to get assistance.

NxLeveL™ Training Network—"tilling the soil of opportunity"
University of Colorado at Denver
Campus Box 128, PO Box 173363, Denver CO 80217-3364
303 556-6652, www.nxlevel.org
Business training program for farm-based enterprises: walks you through the process of creating your business plan, deals with
* marketing, financial planning, management, etc.

SCORE (Service Corps of Retired Executives) & ACE (Active Corps of Executives)—experienced businesspeople providing business management assistance.

Small Business Association (SBA)—and other federal, state and university programs.

Small Business Development Centers—usually attached to university programs—free consulting services, help writing business plan, link to other info and assistance sources. Their mission is to strengthen the small business community.

Small Business Institutes—SBA/University joint programs—help deal with specific problems like marketing resources: structure research, collect information and help interpret it for your situation. Sometimes there is a small fee for research.

General resources for information and assistance

American Farmland Trust
1200 18th Street, N.W. Suite 800, Washington DC 20036
800 431-1499, www.farmland.org
Mission: to stop the loss of productive farmland and to promote farming practices that lead to a healthy environment through education, policy alternatives, helping farmers keep their lands.

Appropriate Technology Transfer for Rural Areas (ATTRA)
800 346-9140, www.attra.ncat.org
A great resource for exploring any for-profit farming venture. A national sustainable agriculture information service jointly funded by the National Center for Appropriate Technology and

the USDA Rural Business Cooperative Service. All services and publications are provided free of cost. Lots of information about production, marketing, organic farm certification and the National Organic Program. Offers a free guide to the organic certification process that covers: a brief history of organic certification, steps in the certification process, how to evaluate a certifier and examples of how fees are assessed. Also available is a reformatted version of the regulations in checklist form to help you work through the National Standard's requirements titled National Organic Program Compliance Checklist for Producers.

Food Institute Report
www.foodinstitute.com
Reports food industry news and trends.

New York Sustainable Agriculture Working Group (NYSAWG)
11 North Goodman Street, Suite 2
Rochester NY 14603
585 271-0490, wmail@nysawg.org
Seeking to create a sustainable environment in which farmers and communities are able to bring quality local food to all.

Northeast Region SARE
802 656-0471, www.uvm.edu/~nesare
Federal program hosted by the University of Vermont. Offers competitive grants to increase knowledge and encourage practices that are profitable, environmentally sound and good for communities. For free informational bulletins: www.sare.org/htdocs/pubs/

Organic Trade Association
PO Box 1078, Greenfield MA 01301
413 774-7511, www.ota.com
Business association representing the organic industry in North America.

Value-added production

Center for Food Science
University of Vermont, Burlington, Vt.
200 Carrigan Building, Nutrition and Food Sciences
Burlington VT 05405-0044
802 656-8300

New York State Food Venture Center
Cornell University
Geneva, N.Y.
NYD Agriculture Experiment Station
W. North Street

Geneva N.Y. 14456-0462 e-mail: necfe@nysaes.cornell.edu
Northeast Center for Food Entrepreneurship
www.nysaes.cornell.edu/necfe
N.Y. State Food Venture Center / Center for Food Science
University of Vermont support food ventures in the Northeast
through: business development & entrepreneurship training,
marketing advice, product process development and technology
transfer, regulatory compliance, labeling, education and outreach,
workshops, counseling.

Value-added products agriculture & natural resources

www.newfarm.osu.edu/management/value.html

Commercial kitchen & co-packing facilities

Massachusetts Avenue Project—Food Ventures Program
382 Massachusetts Avenue
Buffalo NY 14213; (716) 816-0961
Small business and financial planning, one-on-one technical
assistance, licensed, commercial kitchen, access to loan funds.
Nelson Farms – Morrisville Auxiliary Corporation
SUNY College of Agriculture & Technology
PO Box 901
Morrisville NY 13408
315 684-6578 (phone)   315 684-6518 (fax)
Western Mass. Food Processing Center
Franklin County Community Development Corporation
324 Wells St.
Greenfield MA 01301
413 774-7204 x 108

Some good places to do research & find useful resources

Community Food and Agriculture Program Cornell University
www.cfap.org
New strategies for strengthening farms an other businesses,
communities and economies.
Cornell's Small Farms Website
www.smallfarms.cornell.edu
Information for and about small farms: production, marketing,
business management, beginning farmers, working with small
farms, etc.
FoodMAP Online
www.foodmap.unl.edu
Sponsored by the North Central Initiative for Small Farm

Profitability (USDA-funded project). Clearinghouse identifying new markets, alternative agriculture opportunities and locating processing equipment and ingredients.

Food Routes

www.foodroutes.org/toolsforaction.jsp

Provides toolkits and toolboxes marketing materials, research, tips and information.

- Buy Fresh, Buy Local Toolbox: Flagship buy local marketing campaign materials package for food and farming non-profits.
- Buy Local Toolbox: Harvesting Support for Locally Grown Food: Lessons Learned from the "Be a Local Hero, Buy Locally Grown" Campaign
- Communicator's Toolbox: Where Does Your Food Come From? Recipes for Communicating Effectively About American Agriculture

New England Food Safety Education Consortium (NEFE)

www.umass.edu/umext/nutrition/nefe/nefe/index.html

Offers top five university websites for food entrepreneurs.

NOLO

www.nolo.com

950 Parker St.

Berkeley CA 94710

800 728-3555, cs@nolo.com

Makes the legal system accessible to everyone, publishing materials to help people deal with their everyday legal matters.

The Rodale Institute website

www.NewFarm.org

An incredible resource. Stories, research, latest news, online courses, resources, advice, policy updates and opportunities for action and tools: Organic Price Index OPX™, Farm Locator— put yourself on the map and build a free personalized webpage for your farm.

Niche Marketing Texas A&M Factsheet

http://trmep.tamu.edu/cg/factsheets/rm1-2.html

For information on livestock marketing

Cattlemen's Beef Board

303 220-9890, www.beefboard.org

Sustainable Beef Production

www.attra.ncat.org/attra-pub/beefprod.html

Organic Beef Main Information Page

www.agmrc.org/beef/orgbeefmain.html

American Dairy Goat Association
828 286-3801, www.adga.org
Sustainable Goat Production
www.attra.ncat.org/attra-pub/goatwoverview.html
Dairy Goats
www.mda.state.mn.us/mgo/livestock/Dairy_Goats.html
American Meat Goat Association
915 835-2605, www.meatgoats.com
Meat Goat Production
http://pubs.cas.psu.edu/FreePubs/pdfs/ua340.pdf
Meat Goat Resources
www.mgo.umn.edu/livestock/Meat%20Goats.htm
American Horse Council
202 296-4031, www.horsecouncil.org
Horse Business
www.horseandfarmmagazine.com/Farm-finances.html
National Pork Board
515 223-2600, www.porkboard.org
National Pork Producers Council
515 278-8012, www.nppc.org
Sustainable Hog Production
www.attra.ncat.org/attra-pub/Hogs.html
Value-added Pork
www.ciras.iastate.edu/porkmanual
Organic Pork Production
www.attra.ncat.org/attra-pub/PDF/omhog.pd
American Pastured Poultry Producers Association
608 262-0705, www.apppa.org
American Poultry Association
508 473-8769, www.ampltya.com
Small-Scale Egg Production
http://pubs.cas.psu.edu/FreePubs/pdfs/ua335.pdf
Profitable Pasture Poultr
www.sare.org/bulletin/poultry/poultry.pdf
Organic Poultry Main Information Page
www.agmrc.org/poultry/orgpmain.html
American Rabbit Breeders Association
309 664-7500, www.arba.net
Commercial Rabbit Production
www.msstate.edu/dept/poultry/pub1384.htm
American Sheep Industry Association
www.sheepusa.org

Dairy Sheep Association
  802 656-0915, www.dsana.org
Dairy Sheep
  www.attra.ncat.org/attra-pub/dairysheep.html
Milk Sheep Production
  http://pubs.cas.psu.edu/FreePubs/pdfs/ua253.pdf
National Sheep Association
  303 758-3513, www.nationalsheep.org
Small-Scale Sheep Farming
  www.sfc.ucdavis.edu/pubs/brochures/sheep.html
Organic Lamb
  www.blackbellysheep.ord/articles/
  producing%20lamb%20organically.htm
Hair Sheep
  www.kerrcenter.com/kerrweb/publications/2002_proceedings/
  hair_sheep.pdf
Hair Sheep Resources
  www.sheepandgoat.com/hairsheep

For information on alternative livestock marketing

Alpaca Owners And Breeders Association, Inc.
  800 213-9522, www.alpacainfo.com
The Alpaca Registry
  406 755-3158, www.alpacaregistry.net
National Bison Association
  303 292-2833, www.nbabison.org
North American Deer Farms Association
  920 734-0934, www.nadefa.org
American Emu Association
  541 332-0675, www.aea-emu.org
National Ratite Producers Cooperative
  963 372-9383, www.nrpcoop.com
International Llama Association
  303 756-9004, www.llamaweb.com
The International Llama Registry
  406 755-3438, www.llamaregistry.com
American Ostrich Association
  254 647-1645, www.ostriches.org

Northeastern State-specific resources

New York

Earth Pledge
  www.earthpledge.org

Identifies and promotes innovative techniques and technologies that restore the balance between human and natural systems. Farm to Table Initiative promotes sustainable farming practices and builds demand for local, seasonal food.
www.FarmToTable.org

Hudson Valley Slow Food
845 255-4419
email: cedarridge@hvi.net
www.hudsonvalleyslowfood.org
Non-profit organization dedicated to supporting and celebrating U.S. food traditions. Promotes sustainable agriculture and biodiversity through education, outreach, dinners.

New York State Department of Agriculture & Markets
Division of Agricultural Protection & Development Services
1 Winners Circle, Albany NY 12235
518 457-7076, www.agmkt.state.ny.us
Marketing assistance for NY state food producers.

New York State Small Business Development Center
41 State Street, Mezz. Level
Albany NY 12246
800 732-SBDC or 518 443-5398

NOFA-NY
PO Box 880
Cobbleskill NY 12043
518 734-5495, office@nofany.org
www.nofany.org

Regional Farm & Food Project
295 Eight St., Troy NY 12180
518 271-0744, farmfood@capital.net
www.capital.net/~farmfood/
Non-profit organization founded to foster sustainable agriculture and connect farmers and consumers. Sponsors a farmer mentoring program, convenes the NYS Cheese Makers Guild and produces New Connections quarterly and sustainable farms guide.

Small-Scale Food Processors Association of New York
www.nyssfpa.com (check for regional contact information)
A member-driven organization supporting the needs of all small-scale food processors in N.Y. state

Vermont

Vermont Fresh Network—Farm & Chef Partnership

116 State Street, Montpelier VT 05620
802 229-4706, in Vermont 800 658-8787
www.vermontfresh.net
Building innovative partnerships among farmers, chefs and
consumers to strengthen Vermont's agriculture. Publish annual
Dining Guide for local eating & catalog of products available and
participating restaurants for chefs and farmers.

Suggested readings

Resources for Marketing & Management Advice

Celente, Gerald: *Trends 2000*
Drucker, Peter: *Managing in a Time of Great Change*
Gibson, Eric: *Sell What You Sow*
Gladwell, Malcolm: *The Tipping Point—How Little Things Can Make a Big Difference*
Groh, Trauger: *Farms of Tomorrow*
Ishee, Jeff: *Dynamic Farmers' Marketing*
Lee, Andy: *Backyard Market Gardening*
Levinson, Jay Conrad: *Guerilla Marketing, Mastering Guerrilla Marketing*
Macher, Ron: *Making Your Small Farm Profitable*
Nalebuff, Barry: *Coopetition*
Popcorn, Faith: *Popcorn Report, EVEolution*
Salatin, Joel:
   You Can Farm—The Entrepreneur's Guide To Start and Succeed in a Farming Enterprise
   Pastured Poultry Profits: Net $25,000 in 6 Months on 20 Acres
   Salad Bar Beef
   Family Friendly Farming: A Multigenerational Home-Based Business Testament
Whatley, Booker T.: *How to Make $100,000 Farming 25 Acre*
Willis, Harold: *The Coming Revolution in Agriculture*

Changing Paradigms

The Dalai Lama: *Ancient Wisdom Modern World; Ethics for the New Millennium*
Faulkner, Edward: *Plowman's Folly*

REFERENCES

Bangs, David H. Jr. 1989. *The Start Up Guide: A One-Year Plan for Entrepreneurs.* David Bangs, Jr. and Upstart Publishing Company, Inc. Dover, N.H.

Berry, Wendell. 1972. *A Continuous Harmony: Essays Cultural & Agricultural.* New York, San Diego, Harcourt Brace & Company.

Campbell, T. Colin and Christine Cox. 1996. *The China Project—Revealing the Relationship Between Diet and Disease.* New Century Nutrition.

Covey, Stephen. *7 Habits of Highly Successful People.* Audio tape series.

Danaher, Kevin. 2000. *A Clash of Cultures: The McLibel Case.* Global Exchange.

Gibson, Eric. 1994. *Sell What You So—The Grower's Guide to Successful Produce Marketing.* New World Publishing, Carmichael, CA.

Gladwell, Malcolm. 2000. *The Tipping Point—How Little Things Can Make a Big Difference.* Little, Brown and Company, New York, N.Y.

Gleick, James. 1999. *Faster: The Acceleration of Just About Everything.* Pantheon Books, New York, N.Y.

Gussow, Joan Dye. 1991. *Chicken Little, Tomato Sauce & Agriculture—Who Will Produce Tomorrow's Food?* The Bootstrap Press, New York, N.Y. p. 116.

Gyatso, Tenzin, His Holiness the Dalai Lama. 1999. *Ancient Wisdom Modern World; Ethics for the New Millennium.* Abacus Books, London, Great Britain.

Hall, Charles A.S., Cutler J. Cleveland and Robert Kaufmann. 1992. *Energy and Resource Quality—The Ecology of the Economic Process.* University Press of Colorado, Niwot, Colo., p. 77.

Hardin, Garrett. 1968. "The Tragedy of the Commons." *Science,* pp.162, 1243-1248.

Harrison, Allen F. and Robert M. Bramson. 1982. *The Art of Thinking.* Berkley Books, New York, N.Y. pp 101-106, 124.

Henderson, Elizabeth with Robyn Van En. 1999. *Sharing the Harvest—A Guide to Community Supported Agriculture.* Chelsea Green, White River Junction, Vt.

Knight, Richard L. and Suzanne Riedel. 2002. *Aldo Leopold and the Ecological Conscience.* Oxford University Press, New York, N.Y.

pp 50, 173

Levison, Jay Conrad. 1993. *Guerrilla Marketing—Secrets for Making Big Profits From Your Small Business*. Houghton Mifflin Company, New York, N.Y.

Levison, Jay Conrad. 1999. *Mastering Guerrilla Marketing—100 Profit-Producing Insights You Can Take to the Bank*. Houghton Mifflin Company, New York, N.Y.

Longacre, Doris Janzen. 1980. Living More With Less. Herald Press, Scottsdale, Pa.

Macey, Anne. 2000. *Organic Livestock Handbook*. A Project of Canadian Organic Growers, Inc.; Mothersill Printing, Canada.

McChesney, Robert W. 2004. *The Problem of the Media. U.S. Communication Politics in the 21st Century*. Robert W. McChesney, New York, N.Y.

McMath, Robert M. and Thom Forbes. 1998. *What Were They Thinking? Marketing Lessons I've Learned from over 80,0000 New-Product Innovations and Idiocies*. Times Books, New York, N.Y.

Meadows, Donella H., Dennis L. Meadows, Jorgen Randers, William W. Behrens III. 1972. *The Limits to Growth*. Signet, New York, N.Y. pp 53, 95, 161

Nestle, Marion. 2002. *Food Politics*. University of California Press, Berkeley and Los Angeles, Calif.

NxLeveL™ Training Manual. 2000. "Tilling the Soil of Opportunity." NxLeveL™ Education Foundation, Denver, Colo.

Ottman, Jacquelyn A. 1998. *Green Marketing—Opportunity for Innovation*. NTC Business Books, Chicago, Ill.

Phillips, Michael and Salli Raspberry. 2001. *Marketing Without Advertising—Inspire Customers to Rave About Your Business & Create Lasting Success*. NOLO, Berkeley, Calif.

Pollan, Michael. 2002. *The Botany of Desire—A Plant's-Eye View of the World*. Random House, New York, N.Y.

Ponting, Clive. 1991. *A Green History of the World—The Environment and the Collapse of Great Civilizations*. Penguin Books, New York, N.Y. pp 324-241.

Popcorn, Faith. 1991. *The Popcorn Report; Faith Popcorn on the Future of Your Company, Your World, Your Life*. Doubleday, New York, N.Y.

Popcorn, Faith and Lys Marigold. 2000. *EVEolution—The Eight Truths of Marketing to Women*. Hyperion, New York, N.Y.

Redclife, Michael. 1987. *Sustainable Development—Exploring the Contradictions*. Routledge, New York, N.Y. pp 18-19, 118.

Raz, Tahl: *A Recipe for Perfection: America's poshest inn reveals its secrets for satisfying the world's toughest customers.* INC., July 2003, pp 36-37.

Reilly, Kevin. 1992. *Readings in World Civilizations; Volume 1 The Great Traditions.* St. Martin's Press, New York, N.Y. pp 33, 153.

Salatin, Joel. 1998. *You Can Farm—The Entrepreneur's Guide to Start and Succeed in a Farming Enterprise.* Polyface, Inc., Swoope, Va.

Schlosser, Eric. 2002. *Fast Food Nation—The Dark Side of the All-American Meal.* Perennial, New York, N.Y. p 240.

Simmons, Paula. 1991. *Turning Wool into a Cottage Industry.* Storey Communications, Inc., Pownal, Vt. p 89.

Smith, Miranda and Elizabeth Henderson with members of NOFA and Cooperative Extension. 1998. *The Real Dirt: Farmers Tell About Organic and Low-Input Practices in the Northeast.* Northeast Organic Farming Association, Bare, Mass.

Union of Concerned Scientists.1999. *The Consumer's Guide to Effective Environmental Choices.* Three Rivers Press.

U.S. Senate Document #264 published by the 2nd session of the 74th Congress, 1936.

Von Oech, Roger. 1983. *A Whack on the Side of the Head; How to Unlock Your Mind for Innovation.* Warner Books, New York, N.Y.

World Health Organization. "Lack of Fruit and Vegetables Linked to Disease." 22 December 2003, WHO website.

World Health Organization. "Groups Want to Urge Consumers to Eat More Healthy Foods. Notes on the International Meeting to Focus on Fruit and Vegetable Consumption." 13 January 2003, WHO website.

Wyse, Lois. 1983. *The Six-Figure Woman And How to be One.* Ballantine Books, New York, N.Y.

Index

L

M

N

U

U-pick 59
uniqueness of business 35
unprocessed 42
urban society 46

V

value-added 26, 27, 48, 51
values 23
    and goals 65
valuing time, labor, inputs, space 69
vision 24
    clarifying your 64
volume pricing 53

W

waste generation 35
Web, how people read 59
websites 59
    shared 59
Wessel, Kelso 48
whole farm planning 14, 17, 18, 28
whole foods deconstructed 55
Winfry, Oprah 32
women as dominant economic force
    31
women as farm principals 31
wool 48
    skein 53
word of mouth 57
writing, put it in 64

Y

Yellow Pages 57
yogurt 48

NOTES

NOTES

NOTES

NOTES

NOTES